MODEL
BOILERS AND
BOILERMAKING

MODEL
BOILERS AND
BOILERMAKING

K. N. HARRIS
Revised by
MARTIN EVANS

ARGUS BOOKS LIMITED

Argus Books Limited
P.O. Box 35,
Hemel Hempstead,
Herts. HP2 4SS,
England

First Published 1967
Second Impression 1971
Third Impression 1972
Fourth Impression (Paperback) 1974
Fifth Impression (Paperback) 1974
Sixth Impression (Paperback) 1976
Seventh Impression (Paperback) 1977
Eighth Impression (Paperback) 1980
Revised Edition (Paperback) 1982

© Argus Books Ltd 1977

ISBN 0 85242 377 2

Printed in Great Britain
By Unwin Brothers Limited
The Gresham Press, Old Woking, Surrey, England
A member of the Staples Printing Group

Foreword

by

EDGAR T. WESTBURY

THE steam engine, in its many and varied forms, has always been the most popular mechanical working model. Many years ago, Percival Marshall, the founder of the *Model Engineer*, said that every aspiring model engineer should make a point of building a simple steam engine as a foundation for further and more advanced ventures in model engineering; and this precept still holds good. Not only does a steam engine provide a sound exercise in machinery and fitting mechanical components, but it also demonstrates the basic principles of heat engines, and it never fails to interest anyone with a mechanical turn of mind.

But fascinating though the steam engine is, it is not a complete power unit without the addition of some means of providing the working pressure which, so to speak, constitutes its life's blood. Many steam engine models are built which never see a boiler; there may be several reasons for this, among them being the reluctance to subject an elaborate or highly finished model to risk of rust or contamination of its working parts. Demonstration models, which spend all or most of their life in glass cases, are often run on compressed air, and this certainly gives proof of their ability to function in the manner designed. But sometimes apparent problems and difficulties in building a boiler are a deterrent to the constructors. The choice of a suitable boiler for a particular type of engine, and the unfamiliar techniques in cutting, forming and joining its component parts, are often regarded as formidable problems by the inexperienced model engineer.

Apart from a book in the elementary but practical M.E. series published in the early days of model engineering, this is believed to be the first book dealing exclusively and comprehensively with model boilermaking, and it will undoubtedly fill a long-felt want. Written by a practical engineer with a lifetime of experience with both full-size and model steam engines it gives reliable guidance on the design and construction of all types of small boilers; it is a fitting companion to the book Model Stationary and Marine Steam Engines, by the same author.

Experienced model engineers often express divergent opinions on the details of boiler design and methods of construction. But on one thing they are all agreed: the necessity for ample strength in the complete fabricated structure to withstand the maximum pressure ever likely to be encountered for the particular conditions of working. This matter is given due emphasis in Chapter Two of this book, and tests to ensure proper margins of safety are discussed in Chapter Seven. Whether boilers are fabricated by riveting, brazing or other methods, these safety measures should be carefully observed. Sometimes in impatience to get a steam plant working, testing has been neglected or imperfectly carried out; I have known a few cases where boilers have been used in a definitely dangerous condition, and only the protection of that special " Guardian Angel " has prevented serious damage to persons or property.

It should never be forgotten that even a small boiler, or indeed any kind of pressure vessel, is capable of considerable explosive force if it should burst, and may throw missiles, in the form of metal fragments, for a great distance; I have witnessed this in deliberate destruction tests of boilers. This is not intended to be alarmist propaganda; boilers are perfectly safe if constructed in the ways recommended in this book, and it is up to model engineers to keep them so.

On a personal note, I have known Mr. K. N. Harris for many years, and have no doubt about his qualifications to write on this important subject. Having built and experimented with many steam engines and boilers myself, I have learnt about them by the hard way, in the absence of a book such as this to guide me past the pitfalls in both design and construction. Though I have indulged in many arguments with Mr. Harris on points of detail, I have always benefited by his advice and even criticism. I may say there is nothing in this book with which I would take issue; on the contrary, I would recommend it as a valuable addition to every practical model engineer's bookshelf.

PREFACE

IT is more than 60 years since the late E. L. Pearce's excellent little handbook "Model Boilermaking" first appeared; it went through many editions but has long been out of print. Naturally, in the interim, many developments have taken place.

This book is in the nature of an attempt somewhat to expand the original book, and so far as possible to bring the subject up-to-date.

I have endeavoured to provide such information and statistical data, as will enable any intelligent model engineer to design a boiler to meet his own particular requirements, with a reasonable assurance that it will do the job for which it has been designed successfully and efficiently.

Model boilers are, to a large extent, the Cinderellas of model engineering; I think that the principal reasons for this are twofold.

Firstly, there is a great paucity of information about them. Secondly, with the average model engineer, the engine usually comes first, and by the time this is finished and he gets around to making the boiler, he is, quite understandably, in a hurry to see results, and he decides that almost any old receptacle that will boil water and is reasonably steamtight will do.

With regard to the first, it is the principal object of this book to attempt to provide the necessary basic information. With regard to the second, it is my personal opinion that the designing and making of a model boiler, together with its fittings and mountings not only involves just as much skilled craftsmanship as does the making of an engine, though much of it is of an entirely different nature, but is by no means any less interesting.

I am concerned in the following chapters solely with model boilers required to do a job of work. Perfect scale model boilers bear only a very general relationship to working model boilers and obviously anyone who wishes to make such a boiler, for historical record or other purpose, will have either to obtain working drawings or to measure up and make drawings of the original. This sort of work, of course, has its own very definite attractions and calls for a high degree of skilled craftsmanship, but for every one individual who wants to do this, there are probably a hundred or more who want to make a working model boiler.

I have drawn freely upon the work of many other people, too numerous to mention individually, but special acknowledgement must be made in the first place to three great model engineers, now passed on, E. L. Pearce himself, the immortal Hy. Greenly and James Crebbin, known the world over to the older generation of model engineers as

"Uncle Jim." I must make special acknowledgement to Mr. C. M. Keiller for his work on locomotive boiler tube, flue and superheater proportions, and to Messrs. Johnson Matthey & Co. Ltd. for their valuable advice and information on silver solders, and finally to the Calor Gas Co. Ltd. for their assistance in connection with the properties of Calor Gas and information on its use. It is almost certain that some of the statements made and opinions offered in this book will not meet with universal acceptance; this is only natural, the subject is a very wide one and very involved, and there is obvious room for much honest difference of opinion.

I can only say that I have done my best to present facts objectively, and opinions in the light of such knowledge and experience as I have obtained in fifty years of earning my living as an engineer, and more than sixty years of making models, mostly steam.

I certainly would be the last to claim that my ideas are incapable of being improved upon, much less that they are infallible. Least of all would I suggest that any departure from them will be inevitably fraught with dire disaster.

If what follows serves to help aspiring model engineers to make more and better boilers and to stimulate interest in the subject generally, its object will have been achieved.

I have to record my gratitude to my old friend Mr. Edgar Westbury for his kindness in writing a Foreword to this book. With his wide range of interests, knowledge and experience of things mechanical, nobody could possibly have better qualifications and I feel greatly honoured that Mr. Westbury has undertaken this task.

Finally, in a book covering such a complex subject, even with the most careful checking, it is impossible to guarantee freedom from mistakes; if such there be, I must accept responsibility and make my apologies in advance, thereby I trust at least partially disarming my critics.

K. N. HARRIS

CONTENTS

9

1. Properties of saturated steam.

2. Calorific values of various fuels.

3. Tube circumferences and surface areas, etc.

4. Gauges and weights of sheet copper.

5. Recommended screw threads for pipes and fittings.

6. Strength of round copper stays.

7. Safety valve sizes.

8. Properties of J.M.C. silver brazing alloys.

9. Boiler evaporation figures.

DRAWINGS AND SKETCHES

List of Plates

23. Complete firebox with girder roof stays, backhead, front tubeplate and throatplate for 1¾ in. scale narrow gauge model locomotive. The throatplate flange fits *outside* the barrel.
24. Inside view of firebox: note the lower part of the backhead shows a deepening piece added using a coppersmith's joint. Inside the firebox can be seen a security circulator.
25. A special type of watertube boiler for a steam car (full-size, not a model) shown partly tubed. To be fired from the *top* with a spray-burner.
26. Inner firebox backplate with firehole ring brazed in place.
27. Nicholson thermic syphon fitted to locomotive inner firebox, made by Martin Evans.

I. Vertical multitubular boiler with injector feed. Note splendid workmanship and finish

2. Above: " Scotch " marine boiler with donkey feed pump and an excellent range of fittings. Note: door to smokebox with chain to hold it open. Note also how awkward it is to find convenient room for water gauge. A very fine piece of boilermaking

3. Below: Loco firebox showing sif-bronzed foundation ring

CHAPTER ONE

General considerations—Fundamental principles of function-
ing—Combustion and evaporation—Efficiency of model
boilers—Primary features of design to produce an efficient
boiler—Notes on " Scale " and its effects in model work

WHILST there is no intention of cluttering up these pages with masses of figures, formulae and abstract theory it will be obvious to any person of normal intelligence that if one is successfully to design and make a model boiler one must understand the fundamental principles governing its functioning, the characteristics of the materials used in its construction, and the methods involved in making it.

It is, therefore, necessary to provide this basic information and I have endeavoured to do this as simply as possible.

Right at the outset it should be made abundantly clear that a decently designed model boiler, well made of good grade materials, fitted with an efficient safety valve and water gauge, and worked at a pressure not exceeding that for which it was designed is as little dangerous as a sewing machine or a typewriter. On the other hand, a badly designed boiler, carelessly constructed of poor quality material, can be a very dangerous piece of apparatus indeed, one possessing fatal potentialities. Don't be misled either into thinking that so long as a boiler is only working at 20 or 30 lb. per sq. in. there is no need to worry, some of the most disastrous full-size boiler explosions on record have been with boilers working at quite low pressures. The actual working pressure of a boiler has little relation to its potential danger and I would far sooner remain in the vicinity of a well made and maintained boiler working at 1,500 lb. per sq. in. than a badly made and maintained one working at 50 lb. per sq. in.

Let us first consider briefly exactly what happens in a boiler (or for that matter a kettle or saucepan!).

Water is placed within the boiler and a fire lighted beneath it. The heat of the fire passes through the boiler plates or flues or tubes into the water and raises its temperature. The units which the English speaking peoples use to make calculations in this connection are the Fahrenheit Thermometer Scale and the British Thermal Unit. Practically everybody is familiar with the former, but to refresh memories, on this scale freezing point of water is marked by 32° and boiling point of water by 212°.

The British Thermal Unit is the amount of heat necessary to raise the temperature of one pound of water one degree Fahrenheit.*

In passing, though it does not directly apply to boiler problems, one British Thermal Unit (hereinafter referred to as B.Th.U.) would under perfect conditions produce 778 ft. lb. of work.

To return to our boiler, supposing it to contain 1 lb. of water at 62° F. before the fire was lighted, then to bring it to 212° F. boiling point will require the input of 150 B.Th.U. However, there will be no conversion into steam yet; to turn our 1 lb. of water into steam at atmospheric pressure, 14.7 lb. per sq. in absolute, will require the input of another 967 B.Th.U., this quantity being known as the latent heat of evaporation. The steam produced if allowed to expand freely at atmospheric pressure would occupy 26.33 cu. ft.

If, however, it is constrained to a pressure of 100 lb. per sq. in. above atmosphere it will only occupy 3.8 cu. ft.

Turning now to our fuel and taking coal for our example, 1 lb. of good Welsh steam coal, completely burnt, will produce between 14,000 and 15,000 B.Th.U.

We will apply the foregoing to our boiler, supposedly working at 100 lb. per sq. in. (above atmospheric, and from now on any reference to pressure will be to pressure above atmospheric unless otherwise specifically stated) and being fed with water at 62° F. As the pressure of steam is raised, so too is its temperature, in fact an accurate thermometer can be used as an accurate pressure gauge, as will be explained when we come to boiler testing. At 100 lb. pressure the temperature is 338° F. so apart from the 150 + 967 B.Th.U. which we have already put into our water, we still have to find another 126 B.Th.U. to raise the pressure from that of the atmosphere to our 100 lb. working pressure, making a total input for every 1 lb. of water entering the boiler at 62° F. and leaving it as steam at 100 lb. per sq. in. of 150 + 876 + 126 = 1,152 B.Th.U.

The figure of 876 requires explanation, the natural query is why not 967 ?

The answer is that as the pressure goes up the latent heat of evaporation comes down, and at 100 lb. per sq. in., instead of being 967 it is only 876.

Table I gives such properties of saturated steam as will cover practically all requirements of model engineers.

We have now arrived at this point. Our coal can produce, say, 14,500 B.Th.U. per lb. and we require 1,152 B.Th.U. to turn 1 lb. of water at 62° F. into steam at 100 lb. per sq. in.

Therefore, you don't have to be an Einstein to deduce that 1 lb. of good steam coal perfectly burnt in a 100 per cent. efficient boiler would produce about 12.6 lb. of steam at 100 lb. pressure.

Of course, the coal cannot be perfectly burnt, and neither can the boiler transmit all the heat it, the coal, produces into the water but in full-size work an overall efficiency of around 80 per cent. can be

* Strictly speaking this amount of heat is not a constant, but varied slightly with the temperature, but for all practical purposes it can be regarded as a constant.

attained and a good model boiler of reasonable size could hope to reach better than 60 per cent.

That, very briefly, covers the thermal principles of steam generation, sufficiently for our immediate purpose. For those who wish to go more deeply into the matter a most extensive literature is available.

In approaching the design of a model boiler, the first considerations are:

(a) How much steam is required per minute or hour;

(b) At what working pressure.

These two factors are of fundamental importance, the first is necessary to enable us to decide upon the total heating surface required, the second to enable us to decide thickness of shell plates, tubes, etc., size of stays, where required, diameter of rivets, if used, and other structural factors.

This brings us to a matter of first-rate importance, namely, the evaporative capacity of model boilers.

It is a most involved subject and influenced by many factors, and only the most general guidance can be given. In full-size practice, the units used in this connection are pounds of water evaporated (and the desired pressure) per hour per sq. ft. of heating surface (hereinafter referred to as "H.S.").

In model work it has been the custom for years to take the number of cubic inches of water evaporated per minute per 100 sq. in. of H/S.

I believe that Hy. Greenly was the man who introduced this system over 55 years ago; it is not perhaps ideal but it has been established for so long that it is certainly not worth while attempting to change it and it will be used in what follows.

A very generally accepted figure for the evaporative power of model boilers used to be 1 cu. in. of water evaporated per minute per 100 sq. in. of H.S.

Actually this is extremely conservative for any except the simplest types of model boiler fired by methylated spirit. A well-designed model locomotive boiler of, say, 5 in. gauge size, coal fired and working hard will probably evaporate at least three times this rate.

Considering full-size practice for a moment, a Lancashire or Cornish boiler will evaporate about 8 lb. of water per hour per sq. ft. H.S. whilst a modern locomotive boiler will evaporate 20 lb. or more per hour per sq. ft. H.S. when working hard.

Translating these figures to model units an evaporation of 8 lb. per sq. ft. per hour is equal to an evaporation of 2.56 cu. in. per minute per 100 sq. in. H.S., and one of 20 lb. per hour is equal to 6.4 cu. in. per minute per 100 sq. in. H.S.

An evaporation rate of 1 lb. per hour = 0.32 cu. in. per minute.

An evaporation rate of 1 cu. in. per minute = 3.13 lb. per hour.

In connection with these calculations it should be memorised that there are 27.7 cu. in. of water in 1 lb. and 277 cu. in. to the gallon which weighs 10 lb. These latter figures refer to the Imperial gallon which is larger than the American gallon, the latter being 0.83 of the Imperial and therefore weighing 8.3 lb. and containing 230 cu. in. An Imperial pint contains 34.6 cu. in. and weighs 1¼ lb.

On the one hand the model boiler suffers when compared with the full-sized job inasmuch as compared with its cubic contents its radiating surface is considerably greater, and this is aggravated by the fact that in the model the material used is usually copper, which has a much greater conductive capacity for heat than has mild steel (about seven times as much) and the condition is made still worse by the fact that model boilers are frequently unlagged, and even if lagged, their lagging is much less efficient than that of their big brothers.

On the other hand they have an advantage from the use of much thinner plates and tubes and these being usually of copper, the benefit of its high conductivity is of great assistance. In full-size work, with the exception of locomotive inner fireboxes, the material used in boiler construction is almost invariably steel, either mild steel or a nickel steel.

On balance, however, their handicaps outweigh their advantages and their efficiency is considerably lower than is that of the full-sized job.

As a guide, and only a most approximate one, the simpler type of " Pot " boiler, with water tubes, spirit fired, should evaporate 1 cu. in. per minute per 100 sq. in. H.S.

The popular centre-flue launch or marine type of boiler, blowlamp fired, might well evaporate 2 to 2.5 cu. in. per minute per 100 sq. in. H.S.   A model Scotch boiler should do rather better than this, and, incidentally, be far more efficient from a fuel using point of view.   A coal-fired $3\frac{1}{2}$ in. gauge locomotive boiler of good design, working hard, should evaporate at least 3 cu. in. per minute per 100 sq. in. H.S., whilst a good 5 in. or $7\frac{1}{4}$ in. gauge locomotive boiler under similar conditions should attain an evaporation rate up to 5 cu. in. per minute per 100 sq. in. H.S.

A blowlamp-fired watertube boiler of the Scott (not Scotch) type might evaporate anything between $2\frac{1}{2}$ and 5 cu. in. per minute per 100 sq. in. H.S., whilst a medium sized watertube boiler of the Bolsover Express type with a built-in feedwater heater, fired by a silent regenerative or white flame oil burner might exceed 5 cu. in. per minute per 100 sq. in. H.S.

The foregoing figures should only be taken as the most general of guides and results may vary quite widely from them, dependent on all sorts of factors, which themselves may vary very widely too.

It is always safe, when in doubt, to err on the side of making the boiler a bit too big for its job rather than a bit too small.   Other things being equal, the boiler which is comfortably master of its job, will be more economical in fuel, and much less trouble to handle, than will one that is working to the limit of its capacity.

On general principles the most efficient form of heating surface is a flat horizontal plate in direct contact with the flames, slightly inclined water tubes in contact with the fire are about equally effective, as although the upper part of the tube is not directly exposed to the flames, a rapid circulation is set up within the tube which more than compensates.

Surfaces directly exposed to the fire are far more effective than are surfaces not so exposed, as an example, the firebox of a locomotive is around five times as effective in evaporating water as is an equal area of tubes and flues.

Slightly inclined plates and tubes (whether water or flue) are much more effective than are steeply inclined ones.

Water tubes, by the way, should always be inclined even if only slightly so, never horizontal.

When we come to consider the efficiency of a model boiler there is frequently some lack of clear thinking; many people would regard the " efficiency " of a model boiler from the point of view of the amount of steam it can produce per minute or hour, the correct view, however, in considering efficiency is to consider the amount of steam produced at a given pressure and superheat per unit of fuel burnt. A centre flue marine boiler, fired by a powerful blowlamp will produce a lot of steam, but a well designed small locomotive boiler, coal fired, will produce far more steam per B.Th.U. which is the real test of efficiency. It may well be that conditions are such that the wasteful combination of blowlamp and centre flue boiler is unavoidable, and it may do its job most effectively, but it is, thermally, a thoroughly inefficient combination.

This brings out the point that although a very hot flame such as that of a non-silent blowlamp or a steam coal fire under powerful draught will produce rapid evaporation from a given surface, it will do so at the expense of wasted heat units. Other things being equal, the lower the flame temperature the more water there will be evaporated *per unit of fuel burnt*. Forcing the fire of a boiler, whatever the fuel used, will increase total evaporation, but it will inevitably do this at the cost of using a greater quantity of fuel per unit of evaporation.

When it comes to a consideration of specific types of boilers, more will be said about their individual characteristics and potentialities. The object to be aimed at in any boiler is to extract the maximum possible number of heat units from the products of combustion, and, within practical limits, the cooler the gases passing to the chimney, the more perfectly will this be attained. To save anyone being clever(?) this does *not* mean that by artificially cooling the products of combustion you will improve the efficiency of the boiler, what it does mean is that every effort should be made usefully to absorb as much heat as possible whether by way of evaporation, superheating or feedwater heating.

Feedwater heating is somewhat neglected. This is a pity, for carefully carried out it can easily add considerably (anything up to 10 per cent.) to the overall efficiency of the boiler. This subject will be dealt with in a later chapter.

The model steam *engine* is at the best most inefficient, and the model locomotive takes a lowish place, due primarily to the very low piston speed at which it works. A 5 in. gauge locomotive with 7 in. dia. driving wheels running at 10 m.p.h. and having 2½ in. stroke cylinders will have a piston speed of only 200 ft. per minute, a quite hopeless speed for anything approaching reasonable efficiency. A full-size locomotive of modern design in good condition may attain an overall efficiency of 10 per cent. or a little better, it is doubtful if the average model locomotive reaches 2 per cent.

As previously pointed out, however, the model *boiler* can attain quite a reasonable degree of efficiency when properly designed and made.

Boilers vary so widely in design, type and construction that it is quite impossible to lay down hard and fast rules applicable to all cases, but certain general principles can be laid down, conformity with which will at least ensure that the resulting boiler will attain a reasonable efficiency. The following points apply generally:

(1) So design the boiler that when doing its appointed task, it is working well within its peak capacity.

(2) Provide as large a grate area and firebox as possible, but note particularly this should *not* be done at the expense of unduly restricting the water spaces surrounding the firebox.

(3) Provide ample flue area for the egress of the products of combustion.

(4) In constructing the boiler use plates and tubes of as thin gauge as is compatible with safety for the designed working pressure and reasonable durability.

(5) Allow as large a steam space as practicable.

(6) Work at the highest pressure that circumstances will permit.

(7) Embody a feedwater heater.

(8) Lag the outside shell or casing of the boiler as adequately as possible; where scale appearance is not of importance lagging may, and should be overscale.

(9) Make sure that an adequate supply of air can get to the fire and, where possible, arrange some means (dampers) of regulating this.

(10) Where liquid fuel is used, make sure that too much air is not supplied, this simply has the effect of cooling the products of combustion to the great detriment of efficiency.

With the silent regenerative type of burner (where it can be used probably the best form of liquid fuel burner) the ideal arrangement is for all the air to be taken in through the burner mixing tube and working with a closed and airtight firebox, as was done on such steam cars as the Stanley & White.

(11) Particularly with solid-fuel-fired locomotive boilers of $\frac{3}{4}$ in. scale and upwards the fitting of a " brick " arch and a deflector inside the firehole improves efficiency. Furthermore, it helps to prevent ash and unburnt cinders being carried into the tubes and flues choking them and the superheater elements and clogging the smokebox. No doubt spark-throwing is most spectacular, it is equally certainly a nuisance and most wasteful.

(12) With solid fuel the form of firegrate is important, some fuels require more air than others, which involves varying the space between the firebars. Experiment to find the optimum proportions is fairly simple and well worth while. Generally, space between the bars should not be less than width of bars.

Perhaps at this point a few words about " Scale " and its effects might not be out of place.

So far as model engineers are concerned " Scale " always refers to linear scale.

Consider for a moment just what happens when we make a boiler (or anything else of a three-dimensional nature) to a reduced scale, and to do this let us take an actual case.

Suppose we have a full-size boiler 5 ft. dia. 15 ft. long externally fired and presenting two-thirds of its shell to the fire or hot products of combustion and working two-thirds full of water and decide to make a 1 in. scale model of it.

Our full-size boiler shell has a total area of $5 \times \pi \times 15$ sq. ft. = 235 sq. ft. and taking two-thirds of this we have 156 sq. ft. heating surface.

The water content will be 200 cu. ft. Turning now to our model, this will be 5 in. dia. × 15 in. long, one-twelfth the *linear* dimensions of the original;

its heating surface will be $\dfrac{5 \times \pi \times 15 \times 2}{3}$ sq. in. = 156 sq. in. or $\dfrac{1}{144}$

of the full-size job, i.e., $\dfrac{1}{12} \times \dfrac{1}{12}$ or scale squared. Its water content

will be 200 cu. in. or $\dfrac{1}{1728}$ of that of the full-sized job, i.e., $\dfrac{1}{12} \times \dfrac{1}{12} \times \dfrac{1}{12}$ or scale cubed.

Note the result; whereas the full-size boiler has 156 sq. ft. H.S. to 200 cu. ft. content our model has 1·06 sq. ft. H.S. to 0·116 cu. ft. content, or exactly *twelve times as much heating surface* per unit content of water as has the full-size one. Well may a model boiler be expected to be able to steam " scale " sized cylinders. Note, too, that the smaller the scale we work to the greater becomes this discrepancy in favour of the model.

The law is quite simple, linear dimensions vary directly as the scale; areas, surface, or superficial dimensions whatever you like to call them, vary as the scale squared, whilst cubic contents and weights vary as the scale cubed.

This inescapable law runs right through every form of model engineering and a moment's consideration will show that if efficient working is to be aimed at, its effects must be taken fully into account and design modified accordingly.

It has frequently been stated that a model boiler made strictly to scale would not stand the working pressure of a model, usually much less than that of the full-sized job; this is plain nonsense; if an accurate scale model is made of a boiler or any other pressure vessel using materials similar to those used in the prototype, then not only will it be safe for " model " pressures, but for the pressure for which the original was designed. That is cold fact, not theory.

There are many and excellent reasons for not making working model boilers as exact scale reproductions, complication, constructional difficulties and corrosion are obvious ones, lack of strength emphatically is not one.

Another fallacy is that there is no such thing as scale pressure. Scale pressure bears the same relationship to full-size pressure as does the linear scale involved, thus a one-tenth full-size model of a boiler working at 100 p.s.i. has a scale working pressure of 10 p.s.i. A very simple proof is that if you make an exact model of a Lever Weight Safety Valve or a Deadweight safety valve, say, 1 in. scale, it will lift at one-twelfth of the pressure required to make the original blow off.

Here again, nobody works at " scale pressures " as they lead to gross inefficiency, but that does not affect the fact of their existence.

Quite a little has been said about designing a boiler to do a given job, and probably many readers will want to know how to do this.

Obviously our starting point is to find out the amount of steam required per minute (using our model unit of cubic inches per minute as a measure of evaporation).

The simplest way to explain this is by way of illustration.

Let us suppose that a model marine engine is in question; it has a cylinder, double acting 1 in. bore 1 in. stroke and it has been decided to operate it at a working pressure of 75 lb. per sq. in. and at 1,000 r.p.m.

The engine being double-acting at 1,000 r.p.m. the cylinder has to be filled with steam 2,000 times, once *at each end* for each revolution.

It is a simple matter to figure the total swept capacity, or in other words to find the volume of steam which has to be supplied to the cylinder per minute.

Take the area of the bore, in this case 0·785 sq. in., multiply by the stroke in inches, in this case 1 in., and multiply this by 2,000, the number of *strokes* per minute.

Thus 0·785 × 1 × 2,000 = 1,570 cu. in. which is the amount of steam which our engine will require.

Here a word of caution, the owner of the engine may say, " but my engine cuts-off at 75 per cent. of the stroke so it will only need three-quarters of the amount of steam as calculated."

Don't believe it, steam is not a perfect gas and initial condensation and other losses will more than eat up the theoretical savings of early cut-off.

This is not to discourage cutting off, say, at 65-75 per cent. of the stroke, there are great advantages in so doing, notably a much improved freedom from back pressure, due to the improved exhaust cycle, but with small engines if they are really to be worked at the designed speed *and pressure*, it is never safe to calculate on using less than a complete cylinderful of steam and every stroke.

Returning to our calculations, we want 1,570 cu. in. of steam per minute at 75 lb. per sq. in. pressure.

Referring to Table I we find that at 75 p.s.i. 1 cu. in. of water will produce 298 cu. in. of steam, therefore, we shall require our boiler to evaporate $\frac{1570}{298}$ cu. in. of water per minute. Say, 5.3 cu. in. per minute.

Taking a reasonably efficient type of boiler such as a Scotch, Scott or K type (all described in succeeding chapters) capable of evaporating, say, 2 cu. in. per minute per 100 sq. in. H.S., we shall require a boiler having 265 sq. in. H.S. to steam our engine continuously at full power.

A boiler of the first or third type will produce the desired evaporation for less expenditure of fuel than will a Scott boiler.

Incidentally, a well designed and made engine, working under these conditions might easily develop one-fifth brake horsepower, which shows how necessary it is that such an engine should be robustly built and have ample bearing and wearing surfaces.

When it comes to considering the various practical types of boiler some indication will be given of their evaporative potentialities under various working conditions.

As stated earlier, it is always better to err on the side of having a boiler too big for its job than too small: a boiler loses comparatively little efficiency when working well below its maximum capacity but quite a lot when it has to be forced to the limit.

The desirability of working at the highest convenient pressure has already been mentioned. In the first place, given proper engine design considerable thermal economy results, that is to say that for a given expenditure of fuel more power can be obtained by working at, say, 100 lb. per sq. in. than by working at 50 lb. per sq. in., always, of course, assuming that the engine is suitably designed to make efficient use of the steam at the higher pressure and that the valve gear and valve are correctly made and set. Alternatively, less fuel will be consumed to produce the same power from an engine working at 100 lb. per sq. in., than from one working at half the pressure.

Secondary advantages are that at the higher pressures priming (the carrying over of water with the steam) is reduced smaller steam valves and steampipes are required and the steam space in the boiler can safely be reduced, though this should never be carried to excess. At higher pressures, safety valves too can be smaller, a point well brought out by a study of Table VI which gives suitable sizes for these in relation to boiler heating surfaces; incidentally, in settling the size of a safety valve it is always better to err on the side of making it too large rather than too small. For any but the smallest boilers, say, with 100 sq. in H.S. or less, it is advisable to provide two safety valves, one being set to blow off at the normal working pressure, and the other at, say, 5 lb. per sq. in. higher.

A most important point, which is not directly connected with boiler design as such, but which vitally affects the overall efficiency of the plant, is to provide stop-valves and steam supply lines of ample capacity. Every effort should be made to avoid sharp bends and supply lines should kept as short and direct as possible. As a general guide the clear bore of the steam supply pipe should be equal to one quarter of the bore of the cylinder for a single cylinder engine, for a twin cylinder engine this should be increased to about .3 × cylinder bore.

The clear way through the stop valve should be in excess of this to allow for the inevitable frictional losses incurred.

If the best is to be got out of a reciprocating steam plant, it is essential that the pressure maintained in the steam chest when the engine is operating at full power should approximate as closely as possible to that in the boiler, and to ensure this, the conditions outlined above must be fulfilled.

Superheating. One of the greatest helps towards efficiency in the working of small steam engines is the superheating of the steam supply.

Steam in contact with water, as it is in any type of boiler other than the flash, or more correctly " monotube " boiler, is always at the same temperature as the water, and in this condition it is known as saturated steam. The moment we ask saturated steam to do any work it loses heat and a portion of it condenses. If, however, we heat the steam to a higher temperature than its saturated temperature in a vessel separated from the boiler (usually in practice a series of tubes) some of this condensation is avoided and efficiency is much increased.

For models with G.M. cylinders this cannot be carried too far, otherwise the surfaces of the cylinder bore and of the working face of the piston become scored.

With cast-iron cylinders and pistons, having steel or cast-iron piston rings the process can safely be carried much farther.

In any case ample lubrication, preferably via a reliable mechanical lubricator, is absolutely essential, and the oil used must be of a good " superheat " quality.

The clear passage through the superheater should be greater by at leat 50 per cent. than the cross sectional area of the steam supply pipe, as there are considerable frictional losses in tubular superheaters. In conjunction with superheaters, every effort must be made to ensure that they are supplied with dry steam and that carry-over of water is eliminated, or reduced to a practical minimum. Where possible it is advisable to fit the boiler with a well baffled dome and to take the steam from the upper portion of it. Where a dome cannot be used, the best arrangement is a collector pipe situated as near the top of the boiler as possible and having its outer end capped or plugged and a row of small holes drilled in its top surface. This pipe should be as long as possible and the total *area* of the drilled holes should be about 25 per cent. *greater* than the internal cross-section of the pipe.

The carry-over of water into a superheater is fatal to its functioning and I have a very strong suspicion that many of the alleged " super-heaters " in model locomotives are mis-named and at the best do little more than dry the steam, whilst in many cases they are merely an extension of, or addition to, the evaporative surface.

Feedwater heaters and superheaters are dealt with in a subsequent chapter.

Superheating steam increases its volume but for practical model engineering calculations it is as well to ignore this fact. In any case it is by no means easy in small work to determine just what degree of superheat is being attained. It is sufficient to know that any calculations made on the basis of the properties of saturated steam, will have their values improved by superheating.

CHAPTER TWO

Constructional materials and their physical properties. Calculations relating to safe working pressures. General relative proportions (structural)

Materials, calculations relating to safe working pressures, general data on design

COPPER is, par excellence, the model boilersmith's working material, whether in the form of sheet, solid drawn tube, or rod. It is highly ductile, an excellent conductor of heat, and so far as boilerwork is concerned, highly resistant to corrosion. Given a mixture of patience and common sense, it can be shaped and flanged to a degree and with a facility possessed by no other base metal. Its one drawback is that it rapidly loses strength at elevated temperatures.

Rolled sheet copper or solid drawn tube can be taken as having an average tensile strangth of 14 tons per sq. in., but for the purpose of making calculations relating to strength and safety of model boilers, and bearing in mind the loss of strength as temperatures rise it is best to take a figure for tensile strength of not more than 11 tons, say, 25,000 lb. per sq. in.

Of all common metals copper has by far the best thermal conductivity, being, in fact, in this characteristic only exceeded by silver, and that only to the extent of 8 per cent. Relative to mild steel, its thermal conductivity is around seven times greater. This, of course, is an ideal state of affairs for surfaces receiving heat from the fire or flue gases, but the reverse for the outer shell.

Copper can be soft soldered, silver soldered and brazed with great facility; it can also be welded, but the technique involved is outside the scope of the great majority of amateurs and for the purposes of this book will be disregarded.

Copper can be very simply annealed by heating to dull red* and allowing it to cool. More often than not annealing instructions include an injunction to " plunge into cold water " immediately after heating. This is entirely unnecessary and does not affect the annealing process whilst more often than not it will have the effect of more or less seriously distorting the job, especially if its form is somewhat complicated; it may save a few moments of time, but if distortion occurs this is more than lost in putting matters right.

Frequent annealing is an absolute essential in flanging and forming

---

* Dull red in *subdued* light.

25

copper, a matter which will be referred to again in the chapter dealing with the actual methods to be adopted in model boilermaking. Owing to its ductility, copper is an awkward metal to thread either internally or externally. Clean sharp taps and dies, frequent backing of tap or die and use of plenty of lubricant are obvious remedies. Turpentine *not* " turps substitute " is the most satisfactory lubricant I have found, but I believe some people advocate milk.

Quite possibly some of the modern anti-scuffing compounds would help matters. Copper has a high co-efficient of linear expansion, 0·000011 per degree Fahrenheit (mild steel averages around 0·0000068), for this reason as much flexibility should be allowed with stays as possible. Rigid plate stays may work but they can and do lead to trouble and in my opinion rod stays are generally to be preferred, particularly in larger sized boilers. The difference in temperature between the inner surface of a firebox and the outer surface of the boiler shell may well be 1,000° F. or more, so stresses caused by differential expansion are a very real fact and one which cannot be ignored.

One of the heaviest costs in full size locomotive maintenance is caused from the replacement of broken stays around the firebox.

Brass is not to be recommended as a model boiler construction material for either outer shells, fireboxes or water tubes, though good quality solid drawn brass tubes can be used for flues.

Certain qualities of brass are almost as good as copper for our purpose, but the trouble is to be sure you have got such a quality. Other qualities are hopeless as they deteriorate rapidly and can quickly become really dangerous.

Unless the amateur can buy in quantity against specification from a thoroughly reliable manufacturer brass is best left severely alone as a structural boiler material. These strictures do not apply to steam fittings, etc.

Mild Steel is, for larger boilers, a perfectly satisfactory material, but generally speaking it is not recommended for the amateur. It takes a great deal more work to form and flange it, and, incidentally, requires metal formers, whereas hard-wood formers are perfectly satisfactory for copper up to at least $\frac{5}{32}$ in. thick, maybe thicker, but my personal experience does not go beyond this thickness.

Though much stronger than copper and not subject to any serious falling-off in tensile strength at the working temperatures of model boilers, it is still necessary to use heavier plates than would be required with copper, as a substantial allowance must be made for wastage through corrosion. The strength of mild steel plates can be taken as 28-32 tons per sq. in., say, an average of 30 tons or 67,000 lb.

Annealing steel is not nearly so simple as annealing copper, it must be heated to a good red and then allowed to cool *slowly*, covered in lime, a much longer process.

In passing, probably the best way of preserving a steel boiler from corrosion when out of use, is to fill it *absolutely* full of clean boiled water.

Generally mild steel is not recommended as a boilermaking material for the amateur unless he is specially experienced in its working. If it is used, don't forget to make ample allowance for the corrosion factor, generally it is recommended that plates of less than $\frac{1}{8}$ in. thickness should not be used. Galvanising is not recommended, it is not really satisfactory and it has a tendency seriously to reduce the tensile strength of the steel.

Stainless Steel and Stainless Iron probably have considerable possibilities, but so far as model boilermaking is concerned little or no practical experience is available. Given a sound knowledge of the necessary techniques in working them and good workmanship they should be almost ideal, particularly for outer shells. Anyone having practical knowledge and experience of the application to model boilermaking, would confer a favour on the model engineering community by making available his knowledge through the model engineering press.

Monel Metal. This is in many ways the ideal material for outer shells. Monel is a natural alloy of nickel and copper found in Canada. Its average composition is 67 per cent. nickel, 28 per cent. copper plus some manganese and some iron.

It is not only much stronger than copper, its average strength in rolled sheet form being about the same as that of mild steel, but it does not lose its strength at any temperature coming within the ambit of model boiler work.

Its heat conductivity is only about one-sixth that of copper, a great advantage for outer shells and there is no appreciable electrolytic action between it and copper under model boiler working conditions.

It can be formed and flanged with reasonable facility though not so easily as copper. In appearance it has a soft silvery lustre. It can be obtained in sheet and rod form, but not so far as I know in solid drawn tubular form except in small sizes, too small for boiler barrels. It is more expensive than copper, but bearing in mind the fact that it can, for equivalent strength, be used in much lighter gauge than copper (about half) the cost question is not serious.

Monel metal rivets, too, are a commercial article.

It can be brazed and silver soldered without trouble.

Monel metal rod is ideal for stays, it threads much better than copper and is, of course, size for size, more than twice as strong.

Altogether a very worthwhile proposition for the maker of model boilers.

Phosphor Bronze is a very useful material, in the drawn form, for boiler stays, it is stronger than copper and takes threads much better. It can be obtained in wire and rod form in all sizes likely to interest the model engineer.

Jointing materials. Rivets perhaps come first on the list and can be obtained in copper, mild steel, soft iron and Monel metal, with round or countersunk heads. The general rule is to use rivets of similar material to the plates they are joining. Where copper is joined to Monel use Monel rivets, for copper and mild steel copper rivets.

When it comes to soldering and brazing materials there is a very wide range available.

Right at the outset it cannot be too strongly reiterated that under no conditions whatsoever should soft solder be relied upon as a jointing material, it is excellent for making pressure-tight a sound mechanical joint, but at even quite moderate temperatures it loses practically all its mechanical strength, which is very small in any case.

Silver solders come in various grades, with melting points varying from just over 600° F. to around 780° F. Brazing spelters melt at much higher temperatures from about 850° F. upwards.

Generally for amateur use the silver solders are strongly to be recommended in spite of their higher cost. They are much easier to manipulate, run more freely and require much less powerful heating apparatus, and, almost equally important, the less experienced amateur coppersmith is, using them, much less likely to damage the fabric of the boiler through overheating, all too easily done with high melting point brazing materials.

Where joints are silver soldered or brazed there is no need for more than sufficient rivets to hold the separate plates in place, a good hard soldered joint is at least as strong as sheet copper.

The higher quality silver solders in particular not only run very freely, but have the capacity to build up quite a reasonable fillet, this characteristic is often of value, particularly in the fabrication of model boiler fittings and mountings.

The foregoing pretty well covers boiler making materials and their physical properties and we can now consider the vitally important questions of strength and safety.

In all boilers it is usual to allow a comparatively high factor of safety, that is to say that if a boiler is required to work at 100 lb. per sq. in., its plates, stays, etc., are calculated on a basis of its bursting at anything from six to ten times this pressure. A good all round factor for model work is eight and that will be the one adopted in what follows.

Before, however, considering actual calculation methods, something should be said about boiler shapes in relation to strength.

The strongest natural shape for any pressure vessel is a sphere for the simple reason that the internal pressure does not tend to deform it in any way except to increase its size equally in every direction. For practical purposes, however, the spherical form is not a convenient one. The next best form is a cylindrical shell with hemispherical ends, a form much used in the early days in many types of boiler, notably the externally fired so called " egg-ended " boiler.

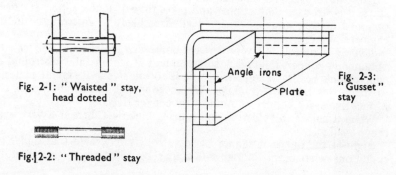

Fig. 2-1: " Waisted " stay, head dotted

Fig. 2-2: " Threaded " stay

Angle irons

Plate

Fig. 2-3: " Gusset " stay

Hemispherical ends are not a very convenient form, but even a small amount of outward dishing gives great additional strength as compared with a flat surface.

Forms in which the internal pressure puts the metal in tension are much stronger than those where it is put in compression. Where flat plates are subjected to stresses, they must be adequately supported by some form of staying. Flat surfaces have the least natural resistance to deformation and are to be avoided wherever possible. Wherever they cannot be avoided they must be well stayed, the inherent strength of the plates should not under any circumstances be relied upon to resist deformation.

Where flat surfaces oppose one another as in the sides and ends of a locomotive firebox, for instance, every endeavour should be made to keep their respective areas equal or as nearly so as possible.

Round stays, particularly those threaded throughout their length, should on no account be over-stressed, a factor of safety for such stays should not be less than ten, and, of course, the calculation must be based on the area at the *bottom* of the thread.

The use of B.A. threads for stays is strongly recommended, as they have well rounded tops and bottoms and are much less liable to flawing than stays with threads having a sharp " Vee " form. The " M.E. " series of 40 threads per inch are also good.

Whilst it means considerably more work, probably the best way of making stays is as shown in the accompanying sketch. If this is done, it is of the greatest importance that there should be a substantial radius where the plain and threaded portions of the stay merge.

Safe *working* loads for copper and monel metal round threaded stays from 7 to 0 B.A. $\frac{1}{4}$ in. $\times$ 40/$\frac{5}{16}$ in. and $\frac{3}{8}$ in. 32 t.p.i. M.E. threads are given overleaf.

The pitching of stays as well as their diameter will depend on the thickness of the boiler plates and on the working pressure. As an approximate guide only, flat areas, such as a locomotive copper firebox, should have stay spacing as follows for working pressures up to 100-120 lb. sq. in.

Fig. 2-4: Single butt riveted and brazed joints	Fig. 2-5: Double butt riveted and brazed joints	Fig. 2-6: Double riveted lap joint

Single butt '

Double   butt

Lap double rivet

$\frac{1}{16}$ in. thick $\frac{1}{2}$ in. centre to centre of stays 6 or 5 B.A.

$\frac{3}{32}$ in. „ $\frac{5}{8}$-$\frac{11}{16}$ in. „ „ „ „ „ 5 or 4 B.A.

$\frac{1}{8}$ in. „ $\frac{3}{4}$-$\frac{7}{8}$ in. „ „ „ „ „ 4 or 3 B.A.

$\frac{5}{32}$ in. „ $\frac{7}{8}$-$1\frac{1}{4}$ in. „ „ „ „ „ 2 B.A.

$\frac{3}{16}$ in. „ $1\frac{1}{8}$-$1\frac{3}{8}$ in. „ „ „ „ „ 2 to 0 B.A.

The above is based on copper plates and copper stays, if Monel metal stays are used the smaller size is applicable in all normal circumstances. With copper no reliance should be made for the initial stiffness of the plate itself. In the great majority of cases due to silver soldering or brazing operations, the plates will be in the annealed condition, in which state copper has very little resistance to deformation.

In calculating the load to be supported by each stay multiply the working pressure in lb. per sq. in. by the area to be supported by the stay. To take a simple example let us suppose we have a small locomotive firebox in which the stays are to be pitched at $\frac{1}{2}$ in. centres and which it is proposed to work at 80 lb. per sq. in. Each stay has to support the load on an area of $\frac{1}{2}$ in. $\times$ $\frac{1}{2}$ in. equal $\frac{1}{4}$ sq. in., 80 lb. $\times$ $\frac{1}{4}$ = 20 lb. which will be the *working* load on each stay. Multiply this by 10 factor of safety and our stay should have a breaking load of 200 lb. Copper as we have already seen under working boiler conditions can be relied on to have an ultimate tensile strength of 25,000 lb. per sq. in.; thus the sectional area we shall require for each stay is: $\frac{200}{25,000}$ sq. in. = $\frac{1}{125}$ sq. in. or 0·0080 sq. in. 5 B.A. has a core diameter of 0·098 in. which gives an area of 0·0073 which is satisfactory for our purpose.

Working from our table we find that a No. 5 B.A. copper stay has a safe working load of 18·7 lb., just on the low side, but with a factor of safety of 10 not sufficiently so to worry us. The next size larger is 4 B.A. with a core area of 0·0092 sq. in. and a safe working load of 23 lb. You pays your money and you takes your choice! In a borderline case of this sort, there is the alternative of using drawn phosphor-bronze in place of copper, the former having a considerable higher tensile strength, and as already mentioned, taking a thread much better.

Gusset stays are largely used to support the ends of " tank " boilers such as Cornish, Lancashire, etc., but for practical model purposes they have little or no application. Sketch shows a gusset stay. (Fig. 2-3.)

This brings us to the strength of boiler shells. In calculations relating to the strength of a boiler shell; so far as the plate is concerned it makes no difference whether it is a rolled plate with a longitudinal joint or a solid drawn tube, that is to say so far as the stressing of the shell is concerned. What does have to be taken into account, however, is the strength of the longitudinal joint, a solid drawn tube having no joint is the strongest form.

The next best arrangement (model practice) is probably one with an inside butt strap riveted and hard soldered, the rivets being only to hold the whole issue together during the brazing or silver soldering operation. If all the contacting surfaces of butt-strap and boiler shell are clean and well fluxed and a proper job is made of the soldering, which entails on the one hand plenty of heat and on the other the avoidance of overheating, the value of the joint should be about 95 per cent. of that of a solid drawn tube. A joint made with a double butt-strap, see sketches of of joints and double or treble rivetted, which means either two or three rows of rivets each side of the joint, should have a strength equal to about 80 per cent. of that of a solid tube.

A double riveted lap joint will have around 75 per cent. and a single riveted lap joint 55 per cent. of the strength of a solid drawn tube, so that it is very obvious that it pays handsomely to use the butt-strap plus brazing technique in making longitudinal joints. Best of all, of course, is to use a solid drawn tube.

The sketches herewith will serve to illustrate the different types of joint referred to. (Figs. 2-4, 2-5, 2-6.)

It has already been agreed to take 25,000 lb. per sq. in. as the safe maximum stress for copper.

We may require to calculate the safe working pressure for a shell of given size and thickness, or on the other hand we may wish to calculate the necessary thickness of material from which to make a boiler of given dimensions to work at a predetermined pressure.

The formulae are quite simple, they are given herewith:

$$T = \frac{P \times D}{2t} \quad \text{or} \quad P = \frac{2T \times t}{D}$$

Where T = Thickness of shell in inches.
P = Working pressure.
D = Internal diameter of shell in inches.
t = Maximum *safe stress** of boiler shell material in lb. per sq. in.

Let us take two examples:

1. We have a solid drawn copper tube 5 in. internal diameter $\frac{1}{8}$ in. thick, what will be a safe working pressure ?

$$P = \frac{2 \times \frac{1}{8} \text{ in.} \times 3125}{5} = 155 \text{ lb. sq. in.}$$

2. We wish to make a boiler with a barrel 6 in. diameter inside to work at 90 lb. per sq. in., what thickness of shell shall we require using a butt-strap and brazed longitudinal joint ?

$$T = \frac{90 \times 6}{2 \times 3125} \times \frac{100}{95} = 0.091 \text{ in.}$$

or $\frac{3}{32}$ in. bare, $\frac{3}{32}$ in. would, of course, be perfectly satisfactory.

Should Monel metal be substituted for copper in this case the thickness could be halved or more than halved!

For practical purposes the strength of rivets in shear can be taken as equal to their tensile strength.

Up to now no mention has been made of screws as a method of making joints. Wherever possible rivets are to be preferred to screws, but in model work it is sometimes not possible to use rivets throughout the construction.

For instance the backhead of a locomotive boiler may well have to

---

* As we have agreed on an average factor of safety of 8, this figure for copper will be $\frac{25,000}{8}$ = 3,125 lb. per sq. in.

be the last plate to be fitted and it will be obvious that in such a case there is no possibility of " holding-up " a rivet from the inside.

In such a case screws must perforce be used, and they should always be of either gunmetal or Monel metal, never brass (unless it is known to be of high grade rolled or drawn type).

Calculations for strength for end or circumferential joints are quite simple.

Consider a cylindrical boiler 5 in. diameter inside (its length does not affect the question). The area of a 5 in. diameter circle is 19·6 sq. in. We wish to work the boiler at 100 lb. per sq. in., obviously the total load on one end or on a circumferential joint, if any, will be 19·6 × 100 lb. = 1,960 lb. Therefore we must provide rivets or screws of sufficient total cross section to carry this load with our agreed factor of safety of 8. Taking the shearing strength of copper as 21,000 lb. per sq. in., then with a factor of safety of 8 the safe working load will be 3,000 lb. per sq. in.

Our total load is 1,960 lb. so we must provide a total cross sectional area with our rivets $= \dfrac{1960}{3000}$ sq. in. $= 0.65$ sq. in. Assume we are using $\frac{5}{32}$ in. diameter rivets, then each rivet will have a cross sectional area of 0·019 sq. in. and we shall thus require a number of rivets $= \dfrac{0.65}{0.019} = 34$.

Thirty-four rivets placed round a circle would give a pitch spacing of about 0·46 in., 34 is not a particularly nice figure for dividing and it would, for practical purposes be well to use 36 rivets.

If screws are used they should have slightly greater nominal strength than rivets owing to the weakening which takes place through thread cutting.

The strength of the screws must, of course, be taken from their *core* diameter. To take the above case No. 2 B.A. screws in gun-metal would be about right.

It is, perhaps, hardly necessary to point out that in the case we are considering, i.e. a plain cylindrical shell boiler with flat ends, the ends would require adequate staying on the principles dealt with earlier in this chapter.

Wherever possible, flat ends should be avoided and slightly dished (outwards) ends used, the greater the dishing the greater the inherent strength, until we come to the hemisphere, which is the strongest possible form of endplate for a cylindrical shell and one that needs no stays at all, unless a single heavy central one is applied to reduce the stresses on the circumferential end joints.

Where a boiler of the Cornish or Lancashire type is concerned, the centre flue or flues, will affect the situation beneficially in two ways.

1. They will reduce the area of the end plate exposed to pressure.

2. Their fastenings will greatly assist in holding the ends to resist pressure.

However, whilst on the face of it this would obviously allow of the number of circumferential rivets being reduced, other considerations arise which affect the situation. Generally, where the strength of the joint is solely dependent on the rivets, i.e. where soft solder or mechanical caulking is relied on to make the joint steamtight rivets should not be

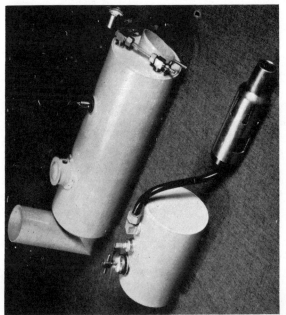

4. Above: Small centre-flue marine boiler with blowlamp and pressure fuel tank

5. Left: Vertical multitubular test boiler for gas firing, with loop superheater, double window plate glass water gauge, steam fountain, main stop valve, direct loaded and lever weight safety valves. Smokehood in foreground, with parts of gas burner

6. Above: Vertical solid fuel fired test boiler, built by Mr. J. Merrit to Mr. E. T. Westbury's design. Note wood strip lagging

7. Below: " Model Engineer " Test boiler with alternative means of firing

spaced further apart than three times their diameter, so this really becomes the governing factor in the case under consideration. Model boiler-making like every form of mechanical or structural engineering inevitably involves compromise, and whenever there is any doubt, err on the safe side.

The diameter of rivets for model boiler work may be taken as follows. For plates $\frac{1}{16}$ in. to $\frac{3}{32}$ in. thick $\frac{1}{8}$ in. dia., $\frac{3}{32}$ in. to $\frac{1}{4}$ in. thick $\frac{5}{32}$ in., $\frac{5}{32}$ in. thick, $\frac{3}{16}$ in.; $\frac{3}{16}$ in. and upwards = plate thickness. Smaller and closer pitched rivets are to be preferred to larger wider pitched rivets in copper boilers.

A great deal of ink has been spilt and a great deal of paper spoilt, in denigrating the riveted and soldered boiler, the general argument being that an all brazed boiler can be run dry without damage. No boiler can be run dry without serious risk of damage, and particularly with a locomotive boiler (brazed) if the water level is allowed to fall below the firebox top there is a most serious risk of the top plate being forced in, or at least badly deformed. If an individual has sufficient ability to build a satisfactory boiler, surely it is not assuming too much, that in operating it he will have sufficient intelligence *not* to let it run dry. In any case a fusible plug, suitably located and kept in good condition, offers a pretty reliable insurance against serious consequences arising from shortness of water.

It has often been alleged that riveted and soft soldered boilers soon begin to leak in use through " differential expansion " (sounds most impressive to the tyro!) causing the solder to break down. If the joint is mechanically sound and close to start with, this is plain nonsense, and this just does not happen.

The boiler of the late James Crebbin's famous *Cosmo Bonsor* (now in the possession of the S.M.E.E.) is over 60 years old, it has led a pretty strenuous life throughout most of that period, it is of riveted and soft soldered construction and is still as tight as a well-corked bottle. That is a practical answer to an untenable theory. For any model boilermaker without powerful heating apparatus at his disposal and without experience of heavy brazing and silver soldering, the riveted and soft-solder caulked boiler is a much safer and more satisfactory proposition than the all-brazed job and he need have no fears about either its safety or longevity, so long as normal intelligence is used in operating it. Where the proper facilities and experience are available the all brazed or hard-soldered job is the goods, where these are lacking the riveted and soft soldered job is a perfectly satisfactory substitute. The halfway house, with brazed firebox, flues and water tubes (if any) and an outer shell riveted and soft soldered is an excellent compromise for those with limited experience and equipment.

CHAPTER THREE

Types of boilers

THERE are in existence literally hundreds of different types of boilers, obviously it would be quite impossible to attempt here to deal with them comprehensively, and if it were, it would be largely wasted effort. Quite apart from this, many of them are of such complicated design and construction as to put them quite outside the realm of practical working propositions in model form.

What will be done will be to describe the more important types likely to be of practical interest to model engineers.

The differing types of boilers can be classified under many headings, such as externally and internally fired, plain and tubular, firetube and watertube, horizontal and vertical, etc., but it is quite impossible to draw hard and fast lines, for one type frequently merges into another, or partakes of the characteristics of more than one other type.

There are for instance boilers which utilise both fire and water tubes, and to draw a line dividing tank boilers from either watertube or firetube boilers is quite impossible. If in what follows there is some over-lapping and lack of clear-cut demarkation, the state of affairs outlined above must take some of the blame.

Let us consider the sketches of differing types in their order. It should be clearly understood that these sketches are purely diagrammatic, intended solely to indicate the general principles of the boilers concerned, and in no case to be regarded as strictly proportional, still less as working drawings!

Fig. 1, the plain horizontal pot, is the simplest of all, commercially it was at one time frequently made without any sort of casing, but this should never be done; a simple sheet metal case lined with asbestos millboard $\frac{1}{8}$ in. to $\frac{1}{4}$ in. thick will just about double its efficiency (or perhaps it would be fairer to say, " halve its inefficiency!"). It is only suitable for firing with methylated spirit or gas. The steampipe should be taken as shown, in a loop through the firebox, over the flame of the lamp. Such a boiler should always be made of light gauge S.D. copper tube, with ends silver-soldered in, and a longitudinal stay supporting the ends should pass through the centre. This stay may well be extended at one end through the back of the case to act as a support. Only half the total area of the barrel within the case should be reckoned as effective heating surface.

This form of boiler is inherently very strong, but usually the type of engine to which it will be supplying steam will be a simple one, not calling for a working pressure of more than 30-40 p.s.i. Figs. 3-1A, 3-1B and 3-1C show simple modifications which individually or in combination will greatly improve its evaporative power. Fig. 3-1A shows the hedgehog arrangement, this consists simply of drilling and tapping a number of holes in the lower half of the shell say $\frac{3}{16}$ in. to $\frac{1}{4}$ in. × 40 t.p.i. and screwing into them short lengths of copper rod allowing say $\frac{1}{4}$ in. to $\frac{5}{16}$ in. of the threaded portion to project into the barrel and leaving $\frac{3}{4}$ in. to $\frac{13}{16}$ in. of the plain portion outside. The effect of this will be a marked increase

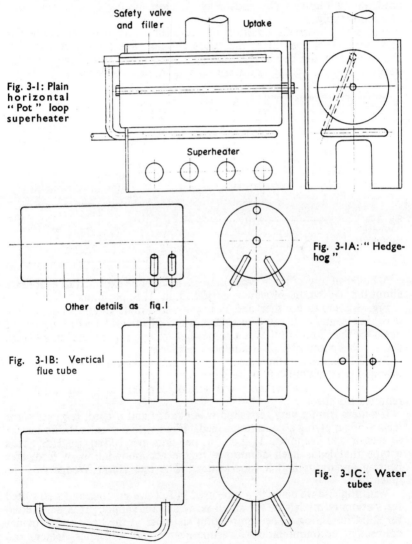

Fig. 3-1: Plain horizontal "Pot" loop superheater

Safety valve and filler

Uptake

Superheater

Fig. 3-1A: "Hedgehog"

Other details as fig. 1

Fig. 3-1B: Vertical flue tube

Fig. 3-1C: Water tubes

in evaporation. If the threads are carefully cut (see hints in Chapter IV) and smeared with a suitable jointing material before screwing tightly home, no trouble will arise through leakage. If the boiler barrel is less than $\frac{1}{16}$ in. thick it will be better to drill plain holes and shoulder down a suitable length of each peg to fit tightly and silver solder them in place.

Fig. 3-1B shows vertical flue tubes, which add to the effective surface. They should be of light gauge S.D. copper and silver-soldered in place. If they are used it is obvious that a central stay cannot be and in this case, either two stays set on the horizontal centre line of the drum may be used, or alternatively the ends may be more deeply dished, and stays omitted entirely.

Fig. 3-1C shows the addition of water tubes and is the most effective improvement of the three, the tubes should have a distinct slope, as shown, and should be not less than $\frac{7}{32}$ in. to $\frac{1}{4}$ in. o.s. dia. and of not too heavy a gauge, certainly not more than $\frac{1}{32}$ in. or 20 S.W.G.

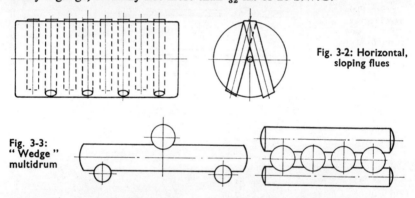

Fig. 3-2: Horizontal, sloping flues

Fig. 3-3: "Wedge" multidrum

A boiler of any of these types may reasonably be expected to evaporate about 0.8 to 1 cu. in. of water per 100 sq. in. H.S. per min.

Fig. 3-2 shows another and not quite so simple modification of the plain horizontal pot, but one that is quite effective. The drilling of the holes for the slanting tubes is a somewhat tricky proposition. In all these cases, tubes should be silver-soldered in place.

Fig. 3-3 shows a rather special type which is useful in a wide shallow draught type of hull. It is perhaps not a very easy constructional job but it is a fast steamer and well suited to pressures up to 120 lb. It requires no stays.

It suffers from a very restricted water range and if used, requires some means of supplying a continuous feed. Fired with a silent paraffin burner or gas, it will evaporate $1\frac{1}{4}$-2 cu. in. per min. per 100 sq. in. H.S. It is a type that lends itself admirably to the accommodation of feedwater heating apparatus and a superheater. The late Harry Wedge was the inventor.

With Fig. 3-4 we come to a type used in full size practice and well suited for stationary models or for small power steam supply. It is best suited for solid fuel firing. The combustion chamber at the back end provides convenient accommodation for superheater and feedwater heater, and

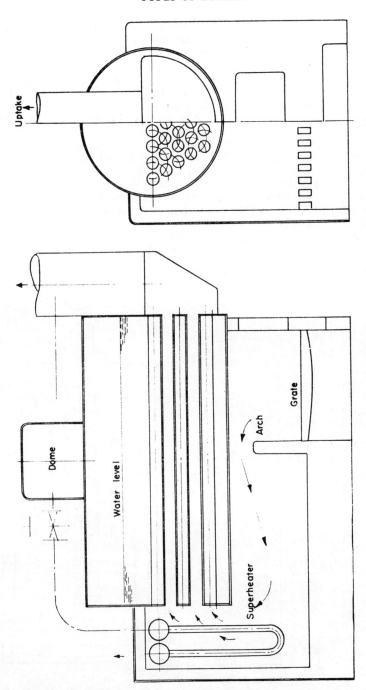

Fig. 3-4: Externally fired return tube boiler with superheater

these can quite easily be made extremely accessible. The casing should be of sheet metal, the upper portion may be lined with asbestos millboard, but the lower portion should be lined with fireclay, or better fire tiles. Care must be taken to make the case airtight, so that air can only gain access to the fire via ashpit or firehole door, leaks in the casing will ruin the draught. The smokebox door too must be quite airtight. In the appendix a dimensioned design for such a boiler is given.

Unless a chimney of some 6 to 8 ft. high is available some form of stimulating the draught will be necessary.

Such a boiler fired with good steam coal should give an evaporation of up to 2 cu. in. per min. per 100 sq. in. H.S. with a good draught through the fire. Construction is simple and lends itself well to the "all hard soldered" principle. Only half the area of the barrel should be reckoned as effective H.S. Proportions of flue tubes are dealt with in Chapter VIII.

It will be noted that all the above boilers are externally fired; before considering internally fired horizontal boilers, we may well take a look at simple externally fired vertical boilers.

Fig. 2-5 shows the vertical boiler in its simplest form, a form much used

Fig. 3-5: Vertical centre flue, no firebox   Fig. 3-6: Vertical centre flue large with cross tubes   Fig. 3-7: Vertical multi-tubular

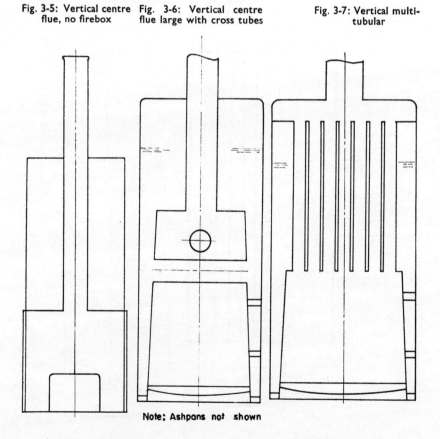

Note: Ashpans not shown

in commercial models of the cheaper (and sometimes not so cheap!) types. It is very simple, but disposes very small heating surface in comparison with its bulk, other than its simplicity it has nothing to recommend it. It should not be relied upon to evaporate more than 0·6 cu. in. of water per min. per 100 sq. in. H.S. and it is only suitable for methylated spirit or gas firing.

Fig. 3-6 is an improved form having a larger flue with cross water tubes and a superheater coil in the upper part of the flue. Strictly the cross tubes should be slightly inclined, but as they are so short, and in any case the boiler is not a type to be forced, horizontal tubes which are simpler to fit, will be found quite satisfactory. Evaporative capacity should be about 1 cu. in. per min. per 100 sq. in. H.S. This type too should only be used with spirit or gas firing.

Fig. 3-7 is another simple improved version of Fig. 3-5 and calls for no explanation, with a firebox well lined with thick asbestos millboard

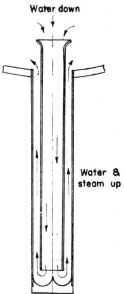

Fig. 3-8: Section field tube

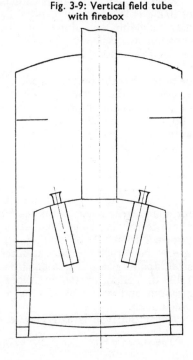

Fig. 3-9: Vertical field tube, no firebox, " crowned " bottom

Fig. 3-9: Vertical field tube with firebox

Note crowned bottom to allow sloped field tubes to sit square to plate

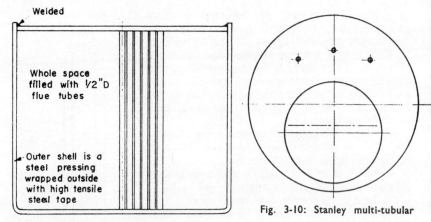

Welded

Whole space
filled with 1/2"D
flue tubes

Outer shell is a
steel pressing
wrapped outside
with high tensile
steel tape

Fig. 3-10: Stanley multi-tubular

it could be fired by a silent type petrol or paraffin burner, but is really more suitable for spirit or gas firing. This boiler, too, should comfortably produce 1 cu. in evaporation per min per 100 sq. in. H.S.

Fig. 3-8 shows a section of a " Field " tube named after its inventor and largely used in steam fire engine boilers. Under suitable conditions it is both effective and efficient. It should preferably not be used at an angle nearer the horizontal than 30 deg.

Where boiler plates of reasonable thickness are used the best method of fixing is by screwing, using a fine tapered thread; 40 t.p.i. up to $\frac{1}{2}$ in. dia. is suitable, and above $\frac{1}{2}$ in. the standard brass thread of 26 t.p.i.* is convenient. Where boiler plates are thin, say, less than $\frac{3}{32}$ in. the tubes can be fixed with " Easiflo."

Fig. 3-9 shows a variation of Fig. 3-5 embodying Field tubes. It will be noted that the bottom of the boiler is coned and the Field tubes stand square with the surface of the cone; this puts them on a slant to the path of the flames and improves their evaporative capacity. The same remarks about firing as made about Fig. 3-7 apply to this type of boiler, and its evaporative capabilities too may be taken as similar.

Fig. 10 shows a plain vertical multitubular boiler. This is more efficient than the single flue type and of course can bulk for bulk contain a greatly increased amount of heating surface; in fact this particular form of boiler can be made to dispose more heating surface per cubic unit of bulk than any other. The Stanley Steam Car Company used a boiler of this form for many years, and speaking from memory, the 10 h.p. version was about 18 in. dia., 14 in. high, contained over 500 $\frac{1}{2}$ in. dia. flue tubes and disposed 66 sq. ft. of heating surface. Incidentally this boiler was of special construction and the outer shell was wrapped with high tensile steel tape to give it increased strength. In tests to destruction, at around 1,400 lb. per sq. in. the flue tubes began to collapse and so released the pressure and so far as is known they never succeeded in rupturing a boiler shell.

Whilst the type is extremely compact it is not particularly efficient;

---

* The Standard brass pipe thread has 26 t.p.i. for *all* sizes.

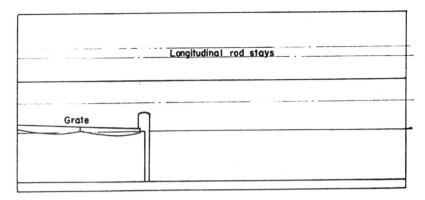

Fig. 3-11: Cornish

on general principles no boiler with straight through vertical flues is, but its efficiency can be considerably augmented by fitting a large feed-water heater in the smokebox to absorb and make good use of heat that would otherwise be wasted. This boiler can be fired by gas or liquid fuel. Its evaporative capacity may be taken at $1\frac{1}{4}$ to $1\frac{1}{2}$ cu. in. per min. per 100 sq. in $\frac{1}{4}$ H.S. if fitted with an effective feedwater heater, but should not be reckoned at above 1 cu. in without this adjunct. The great virtue of the type is its compactness for a given output together with its simplicity.

We may now consider internally fired boilers, and will take first horizontal boilers.

The simplest and about the earliest is the Cornish boiler shown in Fig. 3-11 and, I believe, invented by Richard Trevithick, himself a Cornish-man. This has a single flue passing right through it from end to end, at the front end is situated the firegrate followed by a bridge to deflect the products of combustion, and in the more modern types cross tubes are often fitted in the part beyond the firegrate. These tubes are tapered set with their big ends uppermost and either vertical or at a slight angle. They are known as Galloway tubes, after their inventor. The boiler is carried in a firebrick-lined brick setting and is so arranged that the hot gases from the flue pass down each side of the boiler and return along the bottom (sometimes they pass along the bottom and return along the sides, there is no fixed convention).

This type of boiler has a large water content compared with its heating surface but it is quite reasonably efficient, though it does not take kindly to forcing. It is essentially a coal-fired boiler. In model form it is almost invariably made without the flues surrounding the sides and bottom of the shell and is in consequence much less efficient as a steam producer and far more wasteful in fuel.

Fig. 3-12 shows a model boiler of this type, a type which finds its greatest use in marine work and is almost always blowlamp-fired. It is compact and due to the intense heat of the blowlamp flame has a high evaporative rate per sq. in. of H.S. but it is a terrible fuel waster.

In the appendix, giving detailed designs of model boilers, will be

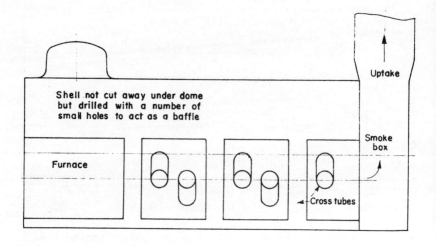

found one for the " K " boiler which I evolved a good many years ago. This is really a Cornish boiler with a metal casing instead of a brick one. From an economy point of view this is a very great improvement on the type shown in Fig. 3-12, as a great deal of heat which with this latter goes to waste directly up the chimney is made good use of in the flue ducts. An additional advantage is the excellent accommodation which it provides for feedwater heater and superheater. So far as solid fuel is concerned, about the smallest sized flue with which this can be used with reasonable satisfaction is 3 in. dia., and as the flue should not exceed $\frac{9}{16}$ of the diameter of the shell this entails a boiler having an outside diameter of, say, $5\frac{1}{2}$ in. If the firebox-flue is made larger than this, the water range becomes too restricted, as does also the steam space. The fitting of a dome to this type of boiler is to be recommended wherever possible.

In its plain form it is often convenient to use, particularly for marine work and its convenience may well outweigh its lack of efficiency. Fired with a blowlamp it may easily evaporate 2 cu. in. per min. per 100 sq. in H.S.

In the more efficient " K " form its evaporation should be $1\frac{1}{2}$ cu. in. per min. per 100 sq. in. H.S. Obviously the value of the heating surface in the outer flues is very much less than that of the firebox and cross tubes, but the *total evaporation per unit of boiler bulk* will be considerably greater with the " K " type than with the plain type and the amount of fuel used for a reasonably high rate of evaporation will probably be halved.

Generally I should regard these two variations of the Cornish boiler as amongst the model engineer's most useful all-round types. The genuine Cornish boiler complete with brick setting has little or nothing to recommend it to the model engineer.

Fig. 3-13 shows the Scotch boiler, used in marine practice from steam launch to Atlantic liner for more than 70 years. Fig. 3-13 shows it in its simplest form with a " dry-back " and a single firebox, a form in which it is admirably suited for model work.

Fig. 3-12: Centre flue, model type, cross tubes

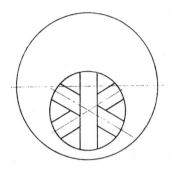

Fig. 3-13A shows it as made in larger sizes, with three furnaces and wet-back combustion chambers, but this form is structurally far more complicated, and from the practical model aspect presents no countervailing advantages.

Incidentally, these boilers have been made of enormous size, over 17 ft dia. with shell plates 2 in. thick and having four furnaces. In the largest sizes, they were frequently made double ended, as shown in Fig. 3-13B. The combustion chambers might be common or separate.

Fig. 3-13C shows a variation due to a man named Inglis, and is one that does have certain advantages for the model engineer. In this it will be seen that after passing into the combustion chamber the gases flow back to the boiler front through a tube of a diameter rather smaller than that of the furnace tube, from this into a smokebox on the boiler front and thence back again to the back end via a series of small flue tubes. The large return flue provides more combustion space and the thermal efficiency is rather higher than it is with the standard type. The main combustion chamber is a little more complicated, but not seriously so.

The Scotch boiler is in every way a splendid type (except where weight is of primary importance) it is a fine steam producer and has a good reserve capacity whilst in its single furnace dry back form, either standard or Inglis, it is a perfectly straightforward constructional job. Where the Inglis form is adopted it is recommended that no watertubes be placed in the furnace tube, but that a number be fixed in the main flue tube. Altogether a splendid type where compactness and fast steaming are required combined with the economical use of fuel. As regards solid fuel, the same remarks as applied to the two preceding types apply to furnace size. A boiler of this type should under good conditions produce an evaporation of 2 to $2\frac{1}{2}$ cu. in. of water per min per 100 sq. in. H.S.

It is worth noting that the dryback combustion chamber not only provides excellent accommodation for feedwater heater and superheater, but excellent access to them and for flue cleaning purposes. The fitting of a dome, though perhaps not so important as with the two previous types, is certainly desirable. Altogether one of the very best of " tank " boilers from the model standpoint.

Probably of all land boilers there have been more Lancashire boilers built in this country than any other, in the first decade of this century. *The Engineer* estimated that there were over 100,000 at work in Great Britain.

Fig. 3-14 shows a Lancashire boiler, which is simply a Cornish boiler with two furnaces instead of one. From the model engineer's point of view it has even less in its favour than has the Cornish boiler, for the

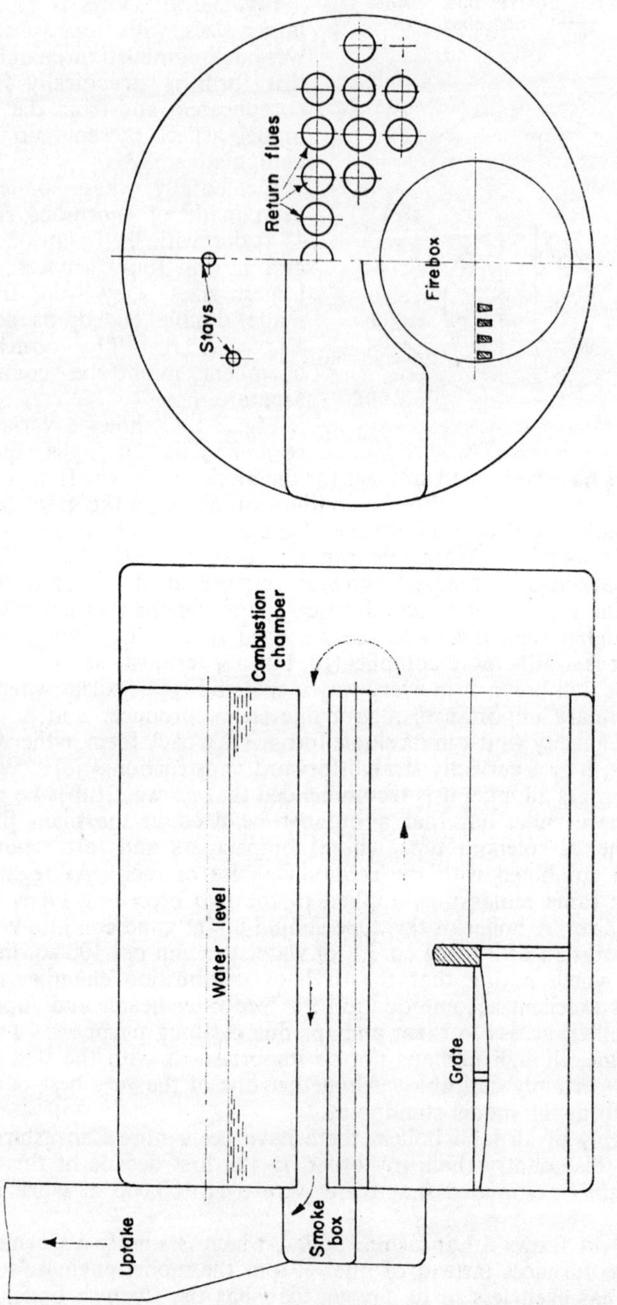

Fig. 3-13: Scotch marine dryback

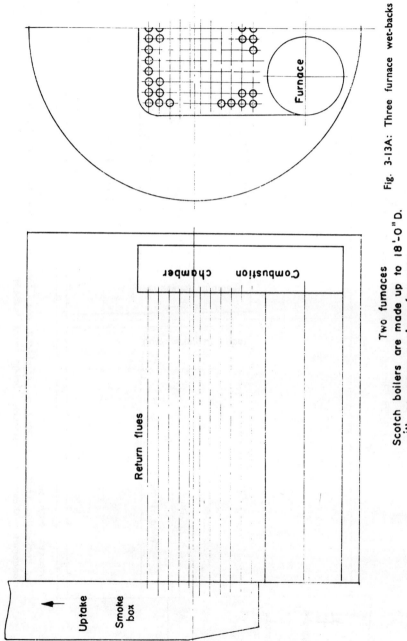

Fig. 3-13A: Three furnace wet-backs

Two furnaces
Scotch boilers are made up to 18'-0"D.
with as many as four furnaces

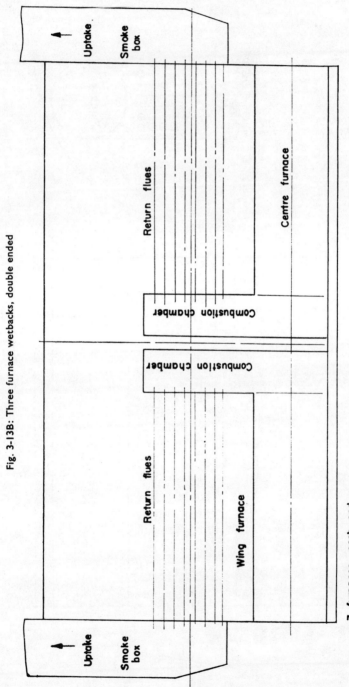

Fig. 3-13B: Three furnace wetbacks, double ended

3 furnaces each end
The combustion chambers may be combined one chamber serving both ends but the
arrangement shown is preferable though more expensive

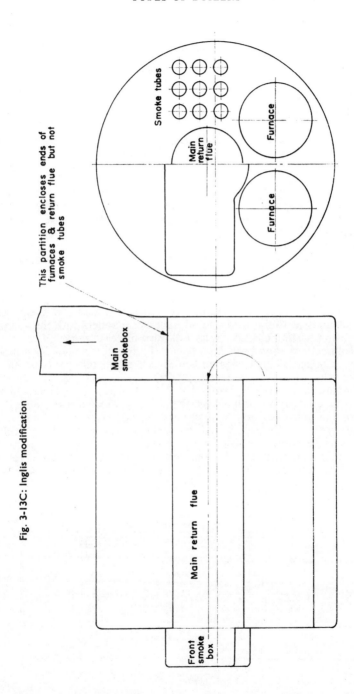

Smoke tubes

Furnace

Furnace

Main return flue

This partition encloses ends of furnaces & return flue but not smoke tubes

Main smokebox

Main return flue

Front smoke box

Fig. 3-13C: Inglis modification

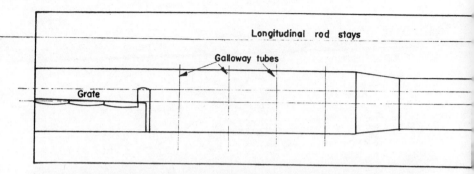

simple reason that it is constructionally more complicated and offers no countervailing advantages. As a practical model steam producer it has nothing to recommend it. Occasionally it has been made with three furnaces, which, from the model point of view, makes it an even less attractive proposition.

Fig. 3-15 shows the Galloway boiler, a widely-used variant of the Lancashire boiler. In this the two furnaces are merged into a kidney-shaped combustion chamber in which are housed a number of Galloway tubes, otherwise in its arrangement and setting it does not differ from the Cornish and Lancashire types. As regards its " model " potentialities, the same remarks apply as to the Cornish and Lancashire boilers with the addition that the combustion chamber is an awkward piece of work.

In volume I of *Wonderful Models* is to be found a design for a model Galloway boiler. This design embodies cast gunmetal endplates, etc., a practice which is not to be recommended.

There are many other horizontal tank boilers but all of them embody the characteristics, in varying combinations, of those already described, and for our purposes may well be disregarded. About the only other type of interest to the model engineer is shown in Fig. 3-15A, and this is a considerable improvement on the type shown in Fig. 3-12.

This brings us to internally-fired vertical boilers and a whole volume might very well be devoted to these alone, in consequence it is only

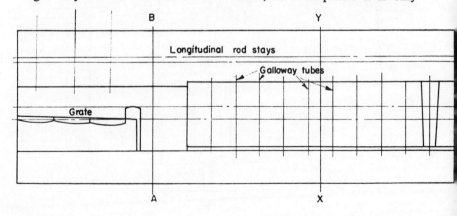

8. Right: Return flue
Marine boiler, show-
ing fittings

9. Below: Marine
boiler with two large
return flues

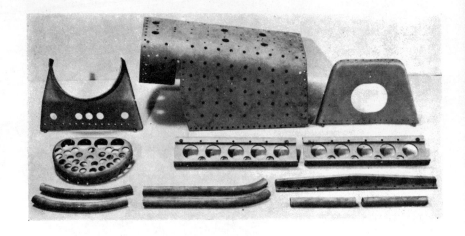

10-11. Disassembled parts for loco boiler, for an American engine

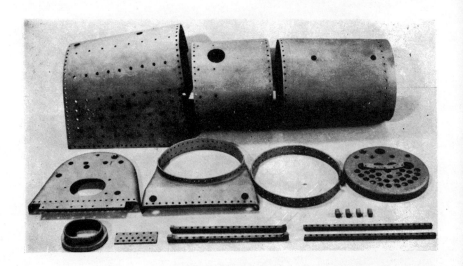

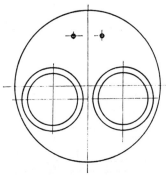

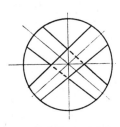

Fig. 3-14: Lancashire

Detail Galloway tubes

proposed to deal with such of them as have attractions from the practical model standpoint.

Fig. 3-16 shows the vertical centre flue type made both with and without cross tubes in the firebox. This type is simple but far from efficient, it is best suited to solid fuel firing. It has had very extensive use the world over, where portability and self-containedness are the ruling requirements.

Where used for model work it should always be of such a size that it is well master of its job, it is not at the best of times an efficient boiler, and when forced becomes even less so. Cross tubes should always be used in a model, for they not only enhance the evaporative capacity, but also improve the efficiency.

Coal-fired, it may be expected to evaporate up to $1\frac{1}{2}$ cu. in. per min. per 100 cu. in. H.S. Fig. 3-17 shows a variation of this boiler which is considerably more efficient than the single flue type. In effect it will be seen to be a combination of the plain multitubular boiler illustrated in Fig. 3-10 and the single flue boiler illustrated in Fig. 3-16. Generally, with this type of boiler, the firebox will be proportionally lower, relative to the overall height than it is with the plain centre flue type. Water tubes in the firebox are not usual. Such a boiler with reasonably long tubes and an efficient feedwater heater in the smokebox, coal-fired, can be expected to evaporate up to 2 cu. in. water per min. per 100 cu. in. H.S.

It is a straightforward fabricating proposition and quite a useful practical type for the model engineer. It is used in full size practice for the same sort of jobs as the centre flue vertical and though more expensive in first cost is a much more economical running proposition.

Fig. 3-18 shows a variation of this boiler in which the flue tubes are

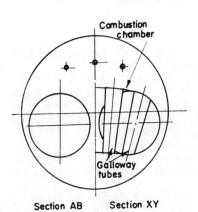

Combustion chamber

Galloway tubes

Section AB   Section XY

Fig. 3-15: Galloway

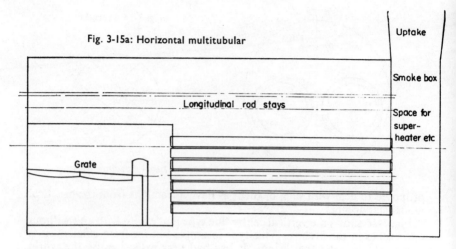

Fig. 3-15a: Horizontal multitubular

Uptake

Smoke box

Space for super- heater etc

Longitudinal rod stays

Grate

kept wholly submerged in water and an enlarged steam space is provided.

It is, thermally, a better proposition than the simpler type shown in Fig. 3-17 but it involves considerably more work and more complicated plate flanging. Nevertheless it is a type that is worth the model boiler-maker's consideration. Its evaporative capacity should be a little better than that of the simpler type, Fig. 3-17. As pointed out in Chapter I, vertical flues are much less efficient than are horizontal flues, and the Cochran boiler, Fig. 3-19, makes use of this fact.

This is a most efficient boiler and is made in quite large sizes. A good coal-fired model should produce at least 2 cu. in. evaporation per min. per 100 sq. in. H.S.

It is a really difficult job to make in model form, and should only be attempted by those having considerable experience in flanging and forming copper plates. That a first class job can be made of it is not in question, the model exhibited on the stand of the North London Society at the 1958 Model Engineer Exhibition was an outstanding example of the coppersmith's art. Apart from its constructional difficulties, a most excellent type for a model.

There are a number of other boilers embodying the principle of horizontal flue tubes, but the Cochran is an excellent representative of a family which differ only in detail and not in principle.

Fig. 3-20 shows a most efficient type of vertical boiler, suitable for either coal or liquid fuel firing. In full size work boilers on this principle have been used in steam launches and on at least two steam lorries, the Robertson, and the St. Pancras. The boiler involves no difficult plate flanging or forming and the assembly of the tubes presents no difficulties. Probably the best method is to utilise a fairly heavy gauge tube for the combustion chamber and thread the tube holes and inner ends of the tubes, 40 t.p.i. for up to ½ in. tubes, and screw them in, expanding the outer ends.

In the appendix is a worked out design for such a boiler for launch or stationary work (it would also make an excellent boiler for a steam rail-

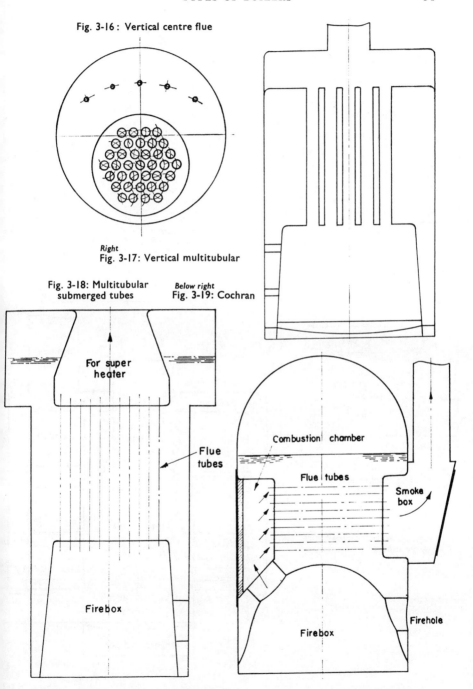

Fig. 3-16 : Vertical centre flue

Right
Fig. 3-17: Vertical multitubular

Fig. 3-18: Multitubular
submerged tubes

Below right
Fig. 3-19: Cochran

For super
heater

Flue
tubes

Firebox

Combustion chamber

Flue tubes

Smoke
box

Firebox

Firehole

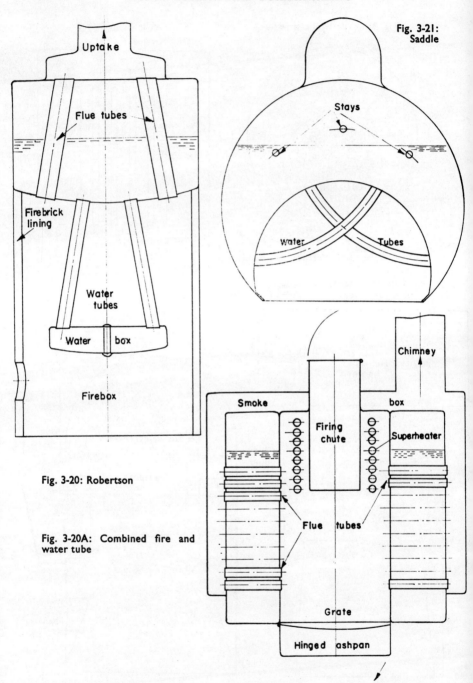

Fig. 3-21: Saddle

Fig. 3-20: Robertson

Fig. 3-20A: Combined fire and water tube

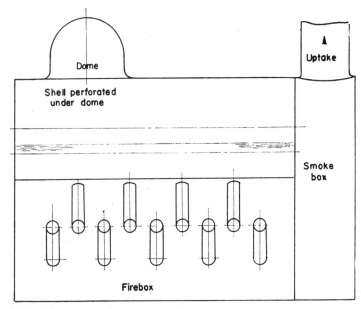

car). This design includes a superheater and a large feedwater heater in the annular flue. Such a boiler, coal-fired, with a good draught should comfortably produce 2 to $2\frac{1}{2}$ cu. in. evaporation per min. per 100 sq. in. H.S. and do this with quite reasonable economy. Altogether it is a type to be thoroughly recommended.

Fig. 3-20A shows a type which admirably instances a boiler embodying the characteristics of tank, firetube and watertube in one unit. It has no particular attractions for the model engineer, and is included more as a matter of general interest than anything else. Fig. 3-20B shows a boiler eminently suitable for marine work and coal firing.

So far we have dealt with boilers having the bulk of their heating surface in firebox and flue where watertubes are included they are subsidiary; the next series rely primarily upon water tubes.

Fig. 3-21 shows a type of boiler not (so far as is known) met in full size practice, but one which is quite useful where simplicity of construction, compactness and good steaming ability are required from a boiler working at a moderate pressure, say not exceeding 50 lb. per sq. in. This type is really only suitable for methylated spirit or gas firing. Should give up to $1\frac{1}{4}$-$1\frac{1}{2}$ cu. in. evaporation per min. per 100 sq. in. H.S.

Fig. 3-22 is a simplified version of the Haystack or Napier boiler, at one time largely used on paddle steamers. This is not too difficult a job for the model boilermaker and it is a fast steaming and, as models go, economical type. In the full size job the top of the boiler was approximately hemispherical in shape and the " waterbox " was quite a complicated piece of plate-work; there were usually four firehole doors. By arranging the outer shell with bolted joints at flue or uptake and at foundation ring as shown in Fig. 3-22A, the outer shell can be removed at any time and the

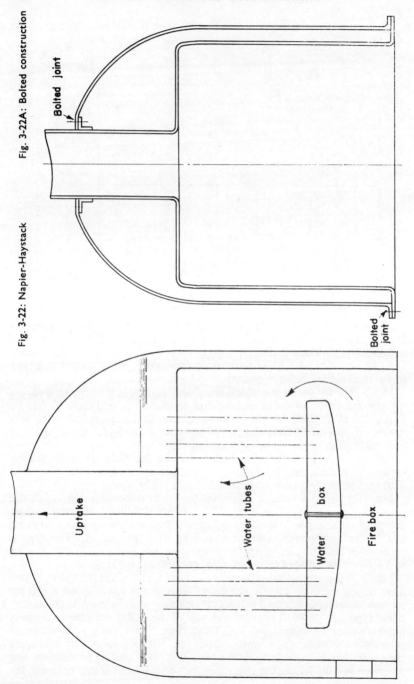

Fig. 3-22A: Bolted construction

Bolted joint

Fig. 3-22: Napier-Haystack

Bolted joint

Uptake

Water tubes

Water box

Fire box

boiler interior thoroughly cleaned. This boiler is primarily suitable for solid fuel firing, but could well be arranged for gas firing or a silent regenerative oil burner, preferably with a totally closed firebox, all the air for combustion being taken in through the induction tube of the burner. This boiler should easily evaporate 2 cu. in. water per min. per 100 sq. in. H.S. It is a type which can be thoroughly recommended.

Fig. 3-23 shows a specialised type of watertube boiler which has been used in the past on steam waggons. It is, as would be expected, a fast steaming boiler, but it has a very small water capacity and requires some reliable means of supplying a constant feed. It is well suited to gas or liquid firing, and equally well to solid fuel firing through a top shute as indicated in the drawing. The two annular rings which form the top and bottom headers would really be best made as pressings, but any reasonably skilful amateur coppersmith could produce them given patience and care by normal flanging methods. The covers should preferably be made with bolted joints, as this allows complete access for cleaning and descaling. In all cases where bolts are used for this kind of work they should be made from good quality drawn gunmetal or phosphor-bronze or better still Monel metal. The type lends itself admirably to the incorporation of a superheater and a feedwater heater. Adequately fired it would produce an evaporation of $2\frac{1}{2}$ cu. in. of water per min. per 100 sq. in. H.S. In larger sizes it would no doubt exceed this figure.

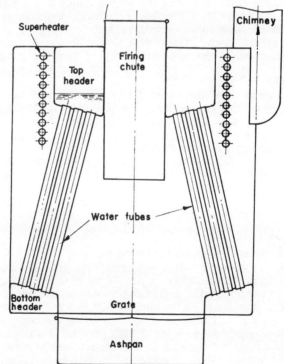

Fig. 3-23: Steam Waggon boiler with water-tube annular feeders

Fig. 3-24 shows another type of steam wagon boiler which is quite a fast steamer, but somewhat complicated in construction; it also has a somewhat restricted steam space and in the smaller sizes might well give trouble through priming. Best suited for oil or gas firing. Evaporation about as Fig. 3-23. Fig. 3-25 shows the well-known Sentinel steam wagon type. This is a splendid steam producer and although the inner firebox is not perhaps an ideal job, it can be made satisfactorily with care and patience. Some suggestions regarding the best way to set about this are included in a subsequent chapter. Can be top fired with coal, as shown in sketch, or fired by gas or oil. Evaporation rate up to $2\frac{1}{2}$ cu. in. water per min. per 100 sq. in. H.S. The outer shell should be affixed with bolted joints as noted for some of the foregoing, and as was done on the original boilers. In every way an admirable prototype.

Fig. 3-26 shows a fire engine boiler, which will be seen to have close affinities with the Sentinel. It differs in having a coned firebox to obtain an increased grate area and using more and smaller water tubes. It was fired from the side and it should be noted that the water space round the firebox was very small actually, only around $\frac{1}{2}$ on the full size job. This was done deliberately with a view to assisting very rapid steam raising. For a boiler in continuous use, it would be a very bad feature indeed, as it would very quickly get furred up, but in the case of a fire engine it was justified, as (a) it was only steamed intermittently and never for more than a few hours at a time, and (b) the standard of maintenance was very high, and due to the outer shell being bolted to the inner structure, it was completely accessible for cleaning and descaling.

Its general characteristics were similar to the Sentinel, only more so, but from the model engineer's point of view the latter is a far better proposition. This fire engine boiler is included chiefly because of its considerable historic interest.

If anyone does make a model of this type particular care should be taken to see that the quality of the feed-water is as pure as possible.

Fig. 3-27 shows the Lune Valley boiler made by the Lune Valley Engineering Co. Ltd. (now no longer in existence) primarily for marine work, launches and small yachts.

It is a very fast steamer and an efficient fuel user, but it is not an easy proposition for the amateur. In model sizes the type of modification indicated in Fig. 3-27A is recommended; the circulation in these boilers is so rapid that in small sizes, unless ample steam space is provided, trouble with priming is almost certain. The space left above the coils in this modification can advantageously be used for superheater and feedwater-heater coils.

This boiler is probably the fastest steaming of all those so far described and with a good oil burner will, depending upon its size, evaporate from 3 to 5 cu. in. of water per min. per 100 sq. in H.S. The latter figure applies only to the larger sizes and is conditional on the use of a really efficient burner. The Lune Valley burner itself is a most interesting job and is referred to in the chapter on Fuels and Firing Methods. Where a compact fast-steaming boiler to work at high pressure is wanted the type is to be unhesitatingly recommended. Needless to say in view of its extremely limited water capacity, continuous feeding arrangements are essential.

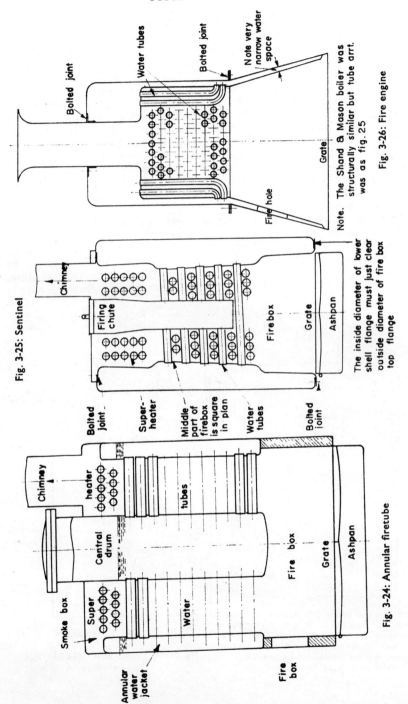

Fig. 3-24: Annular firetube

Fig. 3-25: Sentinel

Fig. 3-26: Fire engine

Note. The Shand & Mason boiler was structurally similar but tube arrt. was as fig. 25

The inside diameter of lower shell flange must just clear outside diameter of fire box top flange

Fig. 3-28 shows the Bolsover Express boiler originally designed and made by the firm of that name, primarily as a steam car boiler (a replacement for the Stanley firetube boiler). It has something in common with the Lune Valley boiler, and if anything has an even more vigorous circulation hence it is, in small sizes, highly desirable to carry out the modification indicated in Fig. 3-27A. It is probably an easier job to make than the Lune Valley. So far as possible all the tubes should be of approximately the same length. Suitable for very high pressures and very high rates of evaporation. Like the Lune Valley primarily for oil (or gas) firing. Would make an excellent boiler for a steam rail car.

Fig. 3-29 shows the Clarkeson thimble tube boiler designed by the late Tom Clarkeson for steam wagon work, but now largely used as a waste heat recovery boiler both ashore and afloat. The boiler is made in two forms: as shown, which is probably the more efficient thermally speaking; and with a central drum and tubes arranged hedgehog fashion, surrounded by an outer casing which is much the simpler manufacturing proposition and in which form it was used for steam lorries. It has interesting possibilities from the model point of view, but the making of the thimble tubes present difficulties, no doubt they could be made in quantity by cartridge producing methods, but this is hardly an amateur proposition. The simplest way that occurs to me is to mount suitable lengths of copper

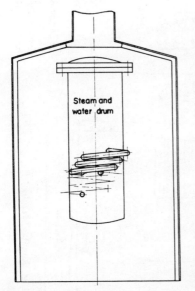

A series of helical coils of steel tube, each of three turns are set in spiral fashion around the drum from bottom to top. Each coil is itself off-set as shown and each successive coil off set relative to the one below. Upper coils filled with steam

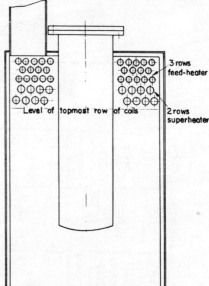

Fig. 3-27: Lune Valley

Fig. 3-27A: Lune Valley, modified, raised drum

tube on a special mandrel, with a
hemispherical end over which the end
of the tube could be spun and any
minute orifice remaining sealed with
brazing spelter.

If made on the annular outer shell
principle as shown in the sketch, the
tubes might well be expanded in place,
if made on the central drum principle
they would be silver soldered. Expanding in this case would be difficult;

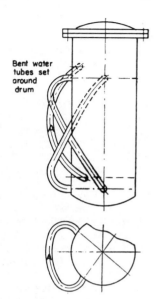

Bent water
tubes set
around
drum

Only two coils shown in this view to avoid con-
fusion each successive row opposite handed.
Shaded LH, plain RH. All coils to be approximately the same length. This means that as
the coils increase in diam. they have fewer
turns. This boiler is suited for oil or gas firing.
Coils should be of an overall length = bore x
260-280. Working pressure for copper max.
200 lb. steel 600 lb.

Fig. 3-28: Bolsover Express. 3-28A : *Illingworth*

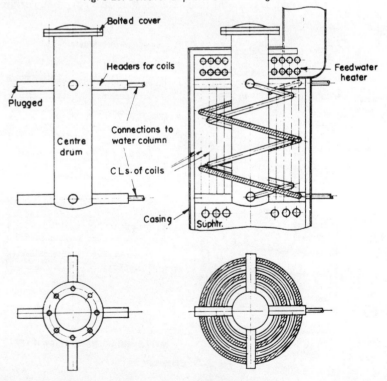

Bolted cover

Headers for coils

Feedwater
heater

Plugged

Centre
drum

Connections to
water column

C Ls. of coils

Casing

Suphtr.

although the inner drum could be at least 2½ in. internal diameter, and
even then quite a problem.

I have had no experience with such a model and have no idea how
it would function, but it would be a very interesting proposition to make
such a model and thoroughly to test it.

In its full-sized form it is a fast steamer and has good thermal efficiency.
Fig. 3-30 is a boiler of the Kingdon watertube type, a fairly simple (as
watertube boilers go) proposition to model and quite an efficient steam
producer. It could be coal fired but is more suitable for gas or oil firing.
Offers good accommodation for superheater and feedwater heater, rapid
circulation and steam production, suitable for high pressure. Precautions against priming are necessary as the circulation is very rapid,
where possible a well baffled dome is advisable. Steam rate 2½ cu. in.
per minute per 100 sq. in. H.S.

Fig. 3-31 shows the well-known Yarrow watertube boiler, excellent in
full size and excellent as a working model. This boiler has a very high
evaporative capacity and can, in model form, be fired with solid fuel,
liquid fuel or gas. Like all watertube boilers it has a restricted water
capacity and requires some form of reliable continuous water feed. It
is necessary, too, to arrange a well baffled steam collecting system, as
the circulation is vigorous. The type is suitable for working at high
pressure and continuous high steaming rates, whilst it lends itself well to
the inclusion of superheater and feedwater-heater. Except in larger units

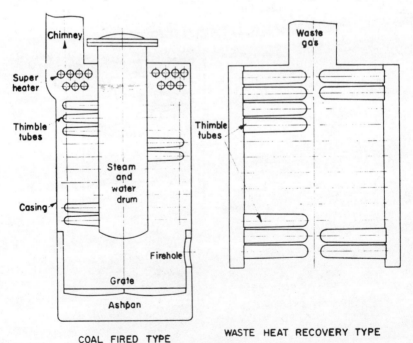

COAL FIRED TYPE   WASTE HEAT RECOVERY TYPE
                    Fig. 3-29: Clarkson

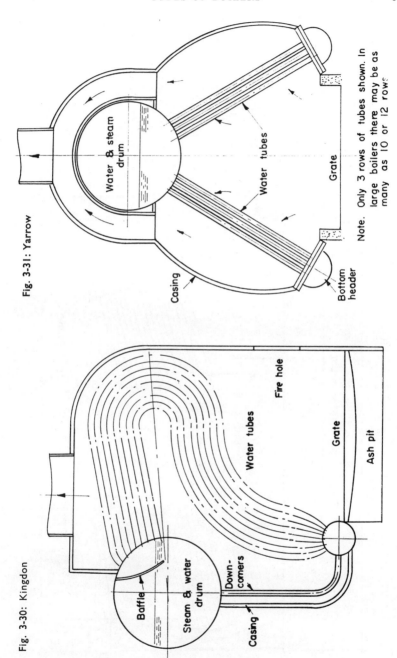

Fig. 3-31: Yarrow

Water & steam drum

Casing

Water tubes

Grate

Bottom header

Note. Only 3 rows of tubes shown. In large boilers there may be as many as 10 or 12 rows

Fig. 3-30: Kingdon

Fire hole

Water tubes

Grate

Ash pit

Baffle

Steam & water drum

Down-comers

Casing

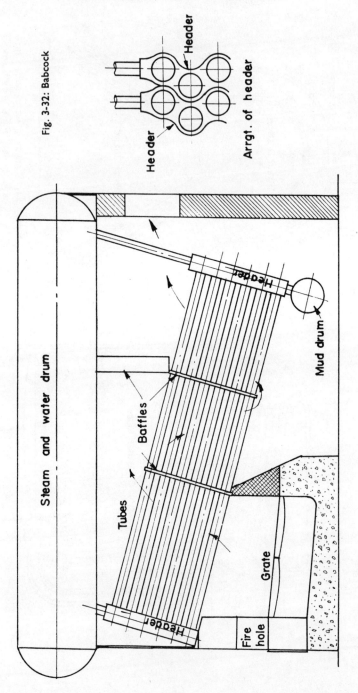

Fig. 3-32: Babcock

of the small-power range, it is best made with only two rows of tubes. The water drums should be made from heavy gauge S.D. copper tube preferably formed thus previous to drilling for the tubes. All hard-soldered construction is practically speaking obligatory for sizes within normal model engineering range. Steam rate up to 4 cu. in. per minute per 100 sq. in. H.S. Where liquid fuel is used the silent regenerative burner is the best proposition. The casing should be heavily lined with asbestos millboard. If solid fuel is to be used, the lower part of the casing should be lined with fireclay, preferably reinforced by the insertion of coarse mesh wire gauze. One of the best of the watertube family.

Fig. 3-32 shows the Babcock, probably one of the most extensively used boilers in full-size pattern for both land and marine work. For model work this type has limited application, it is only suitable for marine work with very large models, its centre of gravity is high and it is not an easy proposition to evolve really satisfactory headers for the tubes, if S.D. *square* copper tubing were available, that would help; castings I never regard as either satisfactory or reliable for any structural part of a boiler. Lends itself well to the installation of superheater and feedwater-heater, reasonably fast steaming, and as the Yarrow, can be fired with solid fuel, liquid fuel or gas. Steaming rate $2\frac{1}{2}$-3 cu. in. per minute per 100 sq. in. H.S. Generally not a particularly good type for the model boiler-maker. There have been a number of designs for this type of boiler in past volumes of the " Model Engineer."

Fig. 3-33 shows the Niclausse, which has been largely used in both marine and land work. It will be apparent from the drawing that this is really a special type of field tube boiler. It is an excellent boiler, one of its great advantages being its complete freedom to expand without creating internal stresses. It is a fast steamer, but from the model engineer's point of view, a satisfactory form of header is not easy to evolve. What is really wanted is a special section of S.D. copper tube which could no doubt be produced if there were sufficient demand though that condition would appear unlikely to arise ! It would, of course, be possible to fabricate such a section using high melting point spelter, but it would not be easy. Steaming rate about the same as Babcock & Wilcox, say, $2\frac{1}{2}$-3 cu. in. per minute per 100 sq. in. H.S. The same remarks regarding superheaters, feedwater heaters and firing methods apply to the Niclausse as to the Yarrow and Babcock types.

Last on our list, Fig. 3-34, shows a type for which I am unfortunately not able to give credit to the inventor, for I have no record of his identity*, but it is a most ingenious design, a fast steamer with an excellent circulation and not too difficult to make; obviously it is an all-hard-soldered proposition. It is suitable for high pressures; like most watertube boilers suitable precuations must be taken to baffle the steam collecting arrangements effectively. Well adapted to the installation of superheater and feedwater-heater. Can be solid, liquid or gas fired. Steaming rate up to 4 cu. in. per minute per 100 sq. in. H.S. Generally a most attractive type for the model engineer.

---

* Although I have an idea it came from Mr. Paris of steam car fame.

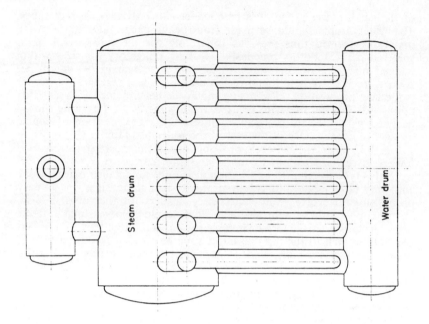

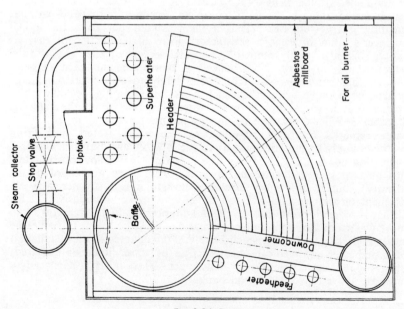

Fig. 3-34: Paris

Finally, all watertube boilers really need reliable continuous feedwater installations, and in the larger sizes, some simple form of auto control for this is well worthwhile considering. The best form, in my opinion, is the simple type used by Stanley's on all their later steam cars, which is dealt with in Chapter Six on boiler fittings and mountings. This type may be made to function in two ways: either by controlling a by-pass on the water delivery line, or, if a donkey pump is used, by controlling the steam supply to it.

Regarding safety valves, having regard to the high evaporative capacity of the water-tube types in general, safety valves should always be of ample capacity, and in general the system of providing two valves, rather than one large one, should be adopted, one valve being set to blow-off at a pressure, say, 5-10 lb. (depending on the working pressure, the higher this is, the larger may be the differential) above the other.

For steady loads and where bulk and weight are not important, the " tank " type boiler is strongly recommended, the Inglis form of Scotch boiler being, in my opinion, the best of all these. Where high steaming rates with low weight and bulk are in question, some form of watertube boiler is almost essential The Stanley type can be used in such circumstances but it is not economical in the use of fuel.

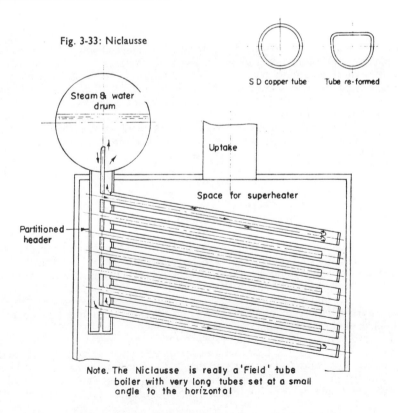

Fig. 3-33: Niclausse

S D copper tube

Tube re-formed

Steam & water drum

Uptake

Space for superheater

Partitioned header

Note. The Niclausse is really a 'Field' tube boiler with very long tubes set at a small angle to the horizontal

CHAPTER FOUR

*Practical methods of construction, flanging and forming
plates—Setting out—Annealing—Riveting*

THERE are quite a number of metal-working processes involved in model boilermaking, these tend to be hand processes rather than machine work, and are certainly none the less attractive on that account; the forming and flanging of plates is a most fascinating process, and whilst it calls for a minimum of equipment, allows for the development of a maximum of manipulative skill.

Before going into detail, let us consider for a moment what is involved in building a model locomotive boiler (the locomotive boiler is chosen because it involves in its construction practically every technique required in model boilermaking).

First of all the various plates have to be marked out to the required shapes, allowance being made for flanging, overlaps for joints, etc., then they must be cut to size. Next, those requiring to be flanged must be annealed. Formers must be cut and shaped for the flanging operations. The barrel, if made from plate, must be rolled to shape and the inner and outer firebox wrappers suitably formed. Tubeplates must be marked out and the holes for the tubes drilled. Plate edges must be cleaned up, tinned if riveting and soft soldering construction is adopted, or fluxed if hard soldering is in question. Stays must be cut and threaded, rivet holes drilled, stay holes drilled and tapped, holes for the bushes for boiler mountings and fittings cut out, tubes and flues cut to length, superheaters built up with their headers, etc., etc., after which follows assembly, brazing, soldering, etc., and finally boiler mountings and fittings must be made and assembled in place with their various pipe connections. Lagging should be applied to all except the smallest boilers and this involves more plate work, in much lighter gauges than used for the structure of the boiler proper, the neat application of flannel or felt under the lagging sheets, and, of course, careful testing, first by hydraulic pressure and then by steam; these tests should, of course, be carried out *before* the lagging is applied.

Surely there is enough in all this to exercise the talents and manipulative skill of any model engineer.

Setting out plates is the first operation and perhaps for that and subsequent work the best method of explaining things will be to take an actual case and follow it right through. For this purpose the 3½ in. gauge ¾ in. scale G.W. type boiler will be taken, as this covers most of the techniques involved in model boiler work.

First of all the barrel should be dealt with. In full-sized G.W. boilers the taper barrels are not true cones, both throatplate and smokebox tubeplate are arranged at right-angles to the base of the barrel.

The bottom of the barrel is horizontal, all the slope being on the top line, thus the barrel is not a true frustrum of a cone and the setting out is quite involved. As a distinguished locomotive engineer remarked many years ago, it is a barbarous piece of plate work. There is, at any rate for the model maker, no advantage whatever in this arrangement, but where, for reasons of scale accuracy anyone wishes to adopt it, much the best method is to set up two thin discs of the appropriate diameter plywood will do for the job, or a stout wooden distance piece at the correct distance apart as indicated in Fig. 4-2.

Having made this, wrap round it a stout sheet of stiff cartridge paper or thin cardboard slightly longer than the finished barrel, and wide enough to overlap, say, ¾ in. at the big end. Fasten in place with a couple of elastic bands, mark round inside the paper along the outside face of each disc in pencil and mark the overlap at the small end. The wrapper should be so applied that its inner edge coincides with the lines A and B. Remove the wrapper trim to the end pencil lines and trim the overlap so that when put in place again it is of equal width throughout, replace to check, if correct use as a template for the barrel plate.

As described this method presupposes either a " lap " or " coppersmith's joint " (to be described later in this chapter). If a " butt " joint is required the sheet of paper should be so cut that there is no overlap and the edges just meet. A word of caution here, it is most probable that when the copper sheet is rolled to shape it will stretch slightly; this does not matter much with the lap or coppersmith joint so long as it is taken care of before the joint is made, but with the butt joint the edges must be suitably trimmed to ensure correct diameters at each end. Your wooden jig can be used to check this.

This particular form of barrel has been dealt with in some detail, as though it is not recommended for freelance working models, nevertheless it is one frequently met with in scale models, not only of modern British locomotives, but with the old Wagon-top American locomotive boilers.

Reverting to our specific job, which has a taper barrel sloping on both its top and bottom lines and is a true frustrum of a cone, the layout is quite simple. The sketch illustrates the barrel as it would be if continued beyond its small end until it came to a point, or in other words, became a complete cone (Fig. 4-1).

The second sketch shows the setting out which once the cone idea is grasped becomes immediately obvious.

This particular barrel is made with a butt joint, but if a lap joint or a coppersmith's joint is preferred add ¾-1 in. to one edge of the plate (a longitudinal edge, of course !). It is suggested that the layout should first of all be done on stiff paper which can be cut to outline, rolled up and checked for correctness, paper is comparatively cheap, copper sheet anything but !

Next we will take the front tubeplate as being the simplest of all the plates. Here we have to make allowance for the flange. The front tube-

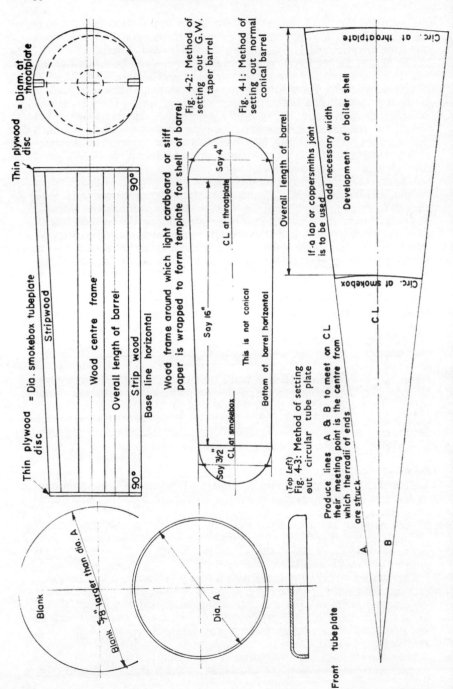

Thin plywood disc = Dia. smokebox tubeplate

Thin plywood disc = Diam. at throatplate

Stripwood

Wood centre frame

Overall length of barrel

Strip wood

Base line horizontal

90°

90°

Fig. 4·1: Method of setting out normal conical barrel

Fig. 4·2: Method of setting out G.W. taper barrel

Wood frame around which light cardboard or stiff paper is wrapped to form template for shell of barrel

Say 4"

C.L at throatplate

Say 16"

This is not conical

Say 3½"

Say 4"

C.L at smokebox

Bottom of barrel horizontal

(Top Left) Fig. 4·3: Method of setting out circular tube plate

Produce lines A & B to meet on C.L their meeting point is the centre from which the radii of ends are struck

Circ. at throatplate

Circ. of boiler shell

If a lap or coppersmiths joint is to be used add necessary width

Development of boiler shell

Overall length of barrel

Circ. at smokebox

C.L

A

B

Blank

5/8" larger than dia. A

Blank

Dia. A

Front tubeplate

plate is made from $\frac{3}{32}$ in. copper and the finished dimensions are as sketch. The diameter over the outside is equal to the inside diameter at the small end of the barrel which is $3\frac{1}{2}$ in., obviously " A " the diameter inside the flange is smaller by $\frac{3}{32} \times 2$, i.e., $3\frac{5}{16}$ in. which, incidentally, will be the diameter of the flanging or forming block. The depth of the flange is $\frac{3}{8}$ in. and you need not be a Senior Wrangler to deduce from this that the required diameter of our blank will be $3\frac{1}{2} + \frac{3}{8} + \frac{3}{8} = 4\frac{1}{4}$ in.

Having dealt with the easiest plate we will take next the most awkward one, the throatplate. This is, incidentally, the one plate that is apt to cause the beginner some difficulty in flanging, as it is flanged both ways so to speak, but we will cross that river when we get to it.

This boiler as detailed is intended to be constructed with a hard soldered firebox and a hard soldered single strap butt joint to the barrel longitudinal seam (see Fig. 2-4; Chapter Two) with the rest of the construction on the riveting or screwing with soft solder caulking principle. There is, of course, nothing to stop anyone with the necessary heating equipment and skill making it an " all hard soldered " job if this is preferred. The flanges of all plates are made of amply sufficient width, or depth if you prefer it, to accommodate rivets with plenty of metal round them, with all hard soldered construction these *could* be reduced, or in some cases done away with altogether, but a good deep flange is always to be preferred and adds nothing appreciable to the cost.

Figs. 4-6 and 4-7 show the layout of the plate blank and of the finished plate and is fully dimensioned. A brief study of this drawing will make apparent the principle of the layout.

These two examples should be sufficient to enable the model boiler-maker to set out any plate he is likely to want in his boiler-work.

Next we will consider the wrapper plates for inner and outer fireboxes. In this particular design the profile of throatplate and backhead are identical, as in turn are those of firebox tubeplate and firebox backplate; this means that the wrapper sheets are straight sided, this, of course,

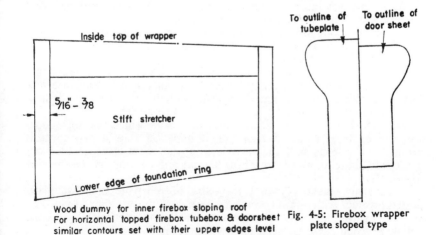

Wood dummy for inner firebox sloping roof
For horizontal topped firebox tubebox & doorsheet
similar contours set with their upper edges level

Fig. 4-5: Firebox wrapper plate sloped type

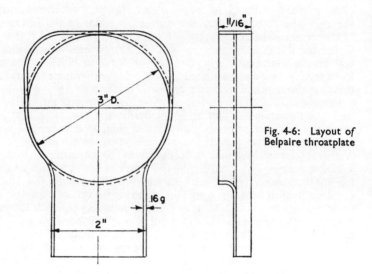

Fig. 4-6: Layout of Belpaire throatplate

excepts the bottom edges of each, which are on the slope upwards from front to back, and are a perfectly straightforward job to lay out. All that is necessary is to run a tape round the edge of each flanged plate and the measurement will give the length of the plate at this point, at least it will give the nominal length, but as it is the inside edge of the plate and the outside edge will be a little longer it is better to add say $\frac{3}{16}$ in. to the nominal length to be on the safe side.

Here again the beginner would be well advised to do his layout on paper first, it is so quickly done and so easily tried out, and in addition is such a perfect insurance against error with expensive material, that there is everything to be said in its favour.

So far, so good; unfortunately for our peace of mind there are many cases where both outer and inner fireboxes are sloped not only in the horizontal plane but in the vertical plane too.

Whilst the wrapper shape can be laid out on the drawing board, not everyone has the necessary knowledge to do this, and in any case it is almost as quick and very much more sure to fall back on the paper template method.

Fig. 4-5 shows a hypothetical inner firebox in which the top slopes downwards from front to back, the foundation ring slopes upwards from front to back and the tubeplate in plan view is wider than the backplate, quite an awkward job to lay out and develop on the drawing board.

Once again, make plywood templates of tubeplate and backplate, fasten together with a strong distance piece making sure they are in their correct relative positions in both horizontal and vertical planes, and finally fit wood strips between the bottom edges.

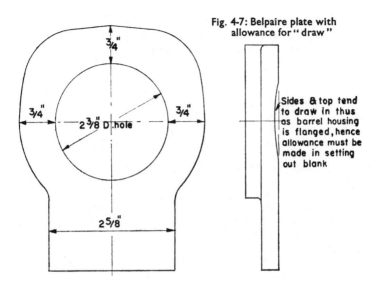

Fig. 4-7: Belpaire plate with
allowance for " draw "

¾"

¾"   ¾"

2⅜" D .hole

2⅝"

Sides & top tend
to draw in thus
as barrel housing
is flanged, hence
allowance must be
made in setting
out blank

You have now, in effect, a dummy inner firebox minus its wrapper.
Once more resort to stiff paper, as there are reverse curves involved the
paper will have to be held in place by a few brads or panel pins, *not*
driven right home, when the paper is lying tight and fair all round, mark
round the outer outline of the dummy firebox, remove and trim to shape,
and you will have an accurate template from which to mark out your
copper sheet.

Where a boiler is of 1 in. scale and over, it pays to make up a strong
wooden dummy outer firebox and inner firebox around which the wrapper
plates can be accurately formed to shape. Where this is done, and it is
really not much trouble, any old scrap timber will do, these dummies
can be used for making the paper templates.

The cutting to outline of copper plates can be done in various ways.
For plates up to perhaps $\frac{3}{32}$ in. thick a powerful pair of hand metal shears
may be used, above this size other methods become necessary. Bench
shears are very useful for this sort of work, though having limitations
inasmuch as they cannot be used for internal curves and being somewhat
expensive for the limited use they are apt to get in the average model
engineer's workshop; nevertheless where possible they are a thoroughly
worthwhile tool. Thicker copper plates can be cut with chisel and hammer,
but I always regard this as a barbarous procedure, bearing about the
same relationship to modern methods as flint knapping does to milling.

Sawing with a narrow bladed saw in a deep frame will cover many
jobs, a saw with moderately fine teeth with ample set should be used and
freely lubricated with cutting oil, turps or milk.

Where curves are too sharp for a normal saw blade, the invaluable
" Abrafile " comes into its own; incidentally this is probably the most
valuable *hand* tool made available to the hand metal craftsman in the
last 50 years.

The old-fashioned method of drilling a series of holes around the outline of the plate, close together and chiselling or sawing between them is also available, but it is a clumsy method for most jobs (firehole rings or foundation rings, cut from the solid plate are perhaps an exception) and involves much more work in trimming up afterwards. Whatever method is used every effort should be made to cut as closely to outline as possible, and thus to save time and energy later. In trimming up plate edges, the milling type of file is to be preferred, for copper is one of the worst metals for file " pinning." Where a milling file is not available it is advisable to oil the teeth before use, and to clear any " pins " at frequent intervals.

In sawing and filing copper sheet it should, so far as possible, be supported on both sides by pieces of wood held in the vice with their edges close to the line to which you are cutting, quite apart from vastly improving cutting conditions, it largely eliminates the fiendish din that this sort of work occasions on a bare sheet. Don't leave any ragged edges or burrs, they are not only likely to cut your fingers, but also to interfere with the mechanical tightness of joints.

Annealing. Nine times out of ten when you find instructions for annealing copper or brass you will be told: " heat it to redness and immediately plunge into cold water." The last part of this injunction is completely superfluous, the only purpose it serves is to save time; furthermore any plate so treated will almost certainly suffer more or less serious distortion, and the time spent correcting this is far more than is saved by " immediately plunging into cold water."

The actual annealing is just as effective if the job is allowed to cool in air as it is when it is plunged into cold water. The heating need not be carried beyond just visible redness, visible in subdued light, *not* in bright sunlight! Annealing should, wherever possible, be done in a gas or blowlamp flame and not in a coal or coke fire. The large burners on the domestic gas cooker are excellent for this purpose.

All plates which have to be bent or flanged should first be annealed, and in flanging several annealings are usually necessary, a matter which will be dealt with fully in the next section.

Flanging and Forming. These are the most fascinating processes in model boilermaking. Copper is a lovely and highly amenable metal and given some knowledge, a lot of practice, plenty of patience and normal intelligence, it can be pursuaded into almost any desired form, far more fantastic forms than are normally ever called for in model boiler work. Incidentally copper-smithing is probably the oldest of all metal-working techniques.

For flanging, having cut out the plates to size and shape, the first requisites are formers. For all thicknesses up to at least $\frac{5}{32}$ in. hard wood is a perfectly satisfactory material on which to flange copper, and unless one is going in for production on a big scale to make metal formers is a waste of time, energy and material. All the plates in the group picture were flanged on wood formers and they run up to $\frac{1}{8}$ in. thick. The formers used were made from mahogany, oak, beech, and in one case applewood from the trunk of an old appletree from my garden, which I cut up and left to season for three or four years before using.

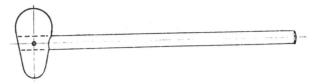

Fig. 4-8:
A round-headed
taper-nosed mallet
for boiler work

Let us start, once again with a simple job, the smokebox tubeplate already dealt with earlier in this chapter.

First as to size, the former will be of a diameter equal to the outside diameter of the flanged plate, minus twice the thickness of the metal $= - (\frac{3}{32}$ in. $\times$ 2). Obviously the best way to produce a circular former is to turn it. The former should be made from stock say 50 per cent. thicker than the depth of the flange, though any increase over this figure within reason is quite satisfactory. The business edge of the former, i.e. the edge over which the flange is to be beaten down, should be radiused, in this case $\frac{1}{16}$ in. radius will suit. As the flanging proceeds this radius is likely to be increased, so it should not be made too large in the first place. As a guide, the initial radius on wood formers should be of a radius equal to about $\frac{2}{3}$ the thickness of the metal to be flanged. A second wooden disc say $\frac{3}{8}$ in. to $\frac{1}{2}$ in. thick and about $\frac{3}{8}$ in. smaller in diameter than the former is required for a backplate; this is not absolutely necessary, but in my opinion most helpful.

The finished tubeplate will have a number of holes in it, and it is best to locate, say, at least three of these which can be used to pass wood screws holding together the former, plate and clamping or backplate, the copper forms the ham in the sandwich. These holes should be drilled initially well undersize as they are liable to " draw " during flanging.

First of all put a fine centre-dot in the centre of the copper blank and from it with a pair of dividers scribe a circle, say, $\frac{1}{16}$ in. larger in diameter than the outside size of the former. Next mark out the positions of three holes as mentioned above, and drill through these holes large enough to clear a No. 6 woodscrew. NOTE: the holes drilled should always be appreciably smaller than the size that will be required in the finished plate, this is important, as particularly if near the flange they are liable to minor distortion and/or stretching.

Anneal the blank, place the copper plate, centre-dotted side up, on the backing plate as near centrally as possible (minute accuracy here is not necessary) mark off the position of the holes and drill the wood to clear No. 6 screws.

Place the copper plate and backing plate on the former and carefully centre, using the scribed circle as a guide, screw together with No. 6 woodscrews. Hold the assembly in the vice with the former facing you and about one-third standing above the vice-jaws. For the actual flanging a hardwood mallet with a round head and a slightly bowed face is recommended, a hammer only being used for finishing. Start and tap the edge of the copper disc towards you, quite light blows are sufficient, work round the edge, whether towards or away from you is purely a matter of personal preference, slack the vice and move the job round, mallet, move around until you have completed the circle; on no account use heavy blows, or attempt to bend the flange over too far at a time 20 deg. to 30 deg. is ample for the first time round (see Fig. 4-8).

With well annealed copper, when you hit it with a mallet (or hammer) it will feel soft and dead, as it is worked it hardens quite quickly and the dead feeling disappears; the moment this happens, it is time to anneal; don't say, "I'll go around just once more," that way lies risk of distortion and/or cracking, crimped edges and general trouble. The whole secret of successful flanging is tied up with frequent annealings and gentle forming, or if you prefer it de-forming.

A moments consideration of the actual job we are discussing will show that the edge of the disc which in the flat measured 3¾ in. around has to be deformed until it only measures 3⅛ " around, this deforming process involves a rearrangement of the internal structure of the metal in the region of the flange to quite a drastic extent and it has just *got* to be done gradually and with frequent annealing.

The final knocking down of the flange tight on to the former is best done with a hammer using the flat face. If the form is true and correct to size and proper care is taken over the job, the outside dimensions and circularity of the flanged portion will be such as to need no further work upon it to make it fit.

The foregoing is a simple straightforward job, ideal on which to begin.

The throatplate is a more difficult proposition, as it is not only a more awkward shape involving uneven displacement of metal, but has to be flanged in two opposite directions. Having cut out and annealed the plate, vertical and horizontal centre lines should be scribed on it on both sides. The circular flange for the barrel should be flanged first.

The formers are rather more elaborate for this job. The one for the barrel flange is simply a piece of ¾ in. or so thick hardwood, say, 1 in. larger all round than the blank plate, with a hole of appropriate size bored in it in this case 3⅛ in. dia., the edge over which the plate is to be flanged being radiused in the same way as the smokebox tubeplate former.

The backing plate should be the same size as the former with a hole about ⅜ in. bigger than that in the former. For convenience in operating this hole will be best bevelled off, as sketch. The backing plate should be not more than ½ in. thick at the outside (Fig. 4-11).

The throatplate has only two holes in it (other than the stayholes which should not be drilled until after erection) which are for washout plugs. These should be marked out and drilled, as with the smokebox tubeplate, for No. 6 wood screws.

Before the hole for the barrel flange is cut in the blank plate, a circle should be scribed from the same centre say 1/16 in. *less* in diameter than the *outside* diameter of the flange; this is to enable it to be correctly located on the former and provide visual evidence that it is so. A sandwich is now made up from former, copper plate and backing piece, taking great care to ensure that the plate is accurately located on the former.

As the holding screws are a long way from the part to be flanged the assembly will have to be clamped with two or three toolmaker's cramps around the portion to be flanged. For this flanging use a mallet shaped as sketch and operate with the smaller end. Proceed round the flange,

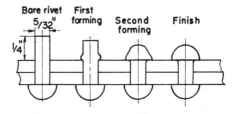

Fig. 4-9: Steps in forming rivets

knocking it down evenly all the way and as soon as it begins to harden, remove from former and anneal. This is a rather awkward flange as there is not much room to operate, particularly as the flange gets down towards its finished shape; again it is chiefly a matter of patience.

The final work to finish the flange tight into its former is best done with a light ball-peen hammer, using the ball end of course. Here it is opportune to mention a matter which will probably arise. When the flange is finished, it will probably be found that the metal at the sides has been drawn in a little as sketch, the extent of this will largely depend on the width of the overlap, the larger this is, the less the tendency. To counteract this tendency the blank plate should be made with an allowance at the appropriate places, as shown in Fig. 4-7.

In this particular case an allowance of about $\frac{1}{8}$ in. at each place should be sufficient. In cases of doubt, err on the generous side, the finished plate may bulge a little at the edges, but this bulge can easily be trimmed off with a milling or bastard file afterwards. Sketches show the effect where no allowance is made and the effect of excess allowance, obviously the latter is to be preferred, as it can so easily be corrected.

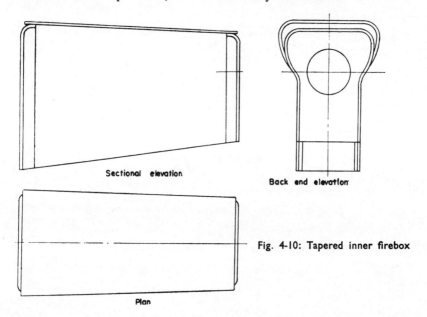

Sectional elevation

Back end elevation

Fig. 4-10: Tapered inner firebox

Plan

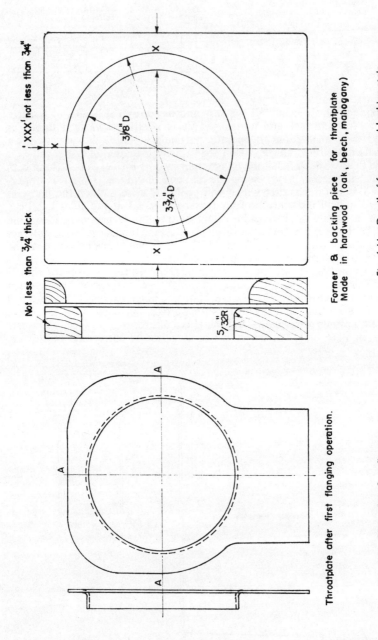

Not less than ³/₄" thick

'XXX' not less than ³/₄"

X

X

X

X

³/₈" D

3 ³/₄ D

5/32" R

Former & backing piece for throatplate
Made in hardwood (oak, beech, mahogany)

Fig. 4-11a: Detail of former and backing strip

A

A

A

A

Throatplate after first flanging operation.

Fig. 4-11: Plate after first flanging

In this same connection, there will be a bulge at the top corners too, which will have similarly to be trimmed, the smaller the radius of these corners, the greater will be the excess, but rather than trying to make an allowance for this, by no means an easy thing to do with any degree of accuracy, let it develop as it will and trim off when flanging is finished. Your plate will now appear as shown in the sketch (Fig. 4-11).

We shall now require a former on which to flange down the outer periphery of the plate and details of this are given in Fig. 4-11. The spigot to fit the barrel flange and the backing strip are necessary to prevent any distortion of the already flanged portion. After annealing, mount plate on former making sure centre-line of plate conforms to centre-line of former and fix backing strip in position.

Then proceed as for the barrel tubeplate, holding the assembly in the vice and working round the flange, be particularly careful not to knock down the straight portions more than the curved parts, the metal around the top corners has to be displaced considerably more than the metal round the sides, and if the latter are knocked down too far too quickly there will certainly be trouble with kinking or frilling on the corners, a trouble once started very difficult to eliminate. Don't forget either that the corners will harden up much more quickly than the straight portions and the moment they begin to do this it is time to anneal. Once again, patience, discretion with the mallet and frequent annealing will keep you out of trouble, and result in a first class job. I have dealt with the forming of this plate at some length as it is certainly the most difficult which will be encountered in any normal model boiler work, and if you make a success of this, any others will be comparatively easy. If you come fresh to flanging work, it is suggested that you should leave this plate to the last, by so doing you will have the invaluable experience gained in flanging the easier plates behind you when you come to the throatplate.

It is certainly not my intention to try to exaggerate the difficulties involved, not to frighten anyone off the job, but it is only fair to point out the pitfalls which lie in wait for the inexperienced. With common-sense, care, and above all patience, there is absolutely nothing to be afraid of. On the other hand if you proceed lightheartedly to " lam " it or " bash " it you will certainly run into trouble. To tell the inexperienced that everything is easy when you know how, is no kindness and just is not true anyhow; it is in fact a fantastically foolish statement, if there were any truth in it you could become a skilled toolmaker, a plus handicap golfer or an Olympic sculler merely by reading books and following the instructions—try it and see!

It is hoped that the foregoing will provide sufficient information to enable anyone of normal ability, successfully to produce satisfactory and accurate flanged plates and we can pass on to methods of making joints.

Whilst solid drawn tubing is the ideal material for boiler barrels, it is not always available in the sizes wanted for a particular job and in any case it is not much use where a taper barrel is wanted, as it so frequently is on models of modern locomotives. I am aware that in the past taper solid drawn tubes for this purpose have been available on the model market in a limited range of sizes, but these seem to have disappeared and in any case the choice was much restricted. I am also aware that it has been recommended that taper barrels should be made by selecting a piece of S.D. tube of a diameter equal to the big end of the barrel, cutting out a wedge-shaped strip longitudinally closing the gap and making a butt-joint along the cut edges. Frankly this strikes one as rather like taking a ticket from Kings Cross to Glasgow and re-booking thence to York, instead of booking to York direct in the first place.

For taper barrels the obvious way is to roll them from sheet metal. For making the longitudinal joint there are two methods both equally good, (a) the butt joint with an inside cover strip lightly riveted and the whole issue silver soldered with a high melting point solder, such as Johnson Mattley's B6 with a tensile strength of 28 tons and a melting range 790-830° C. which has the advantage of being comparatively cheap; (b) by means of a " Coppersmith's Joint." This joint is illustrated by the accompanying sketch (Fig. 4-12).

A and B = circumferences at big and little ends of barrel C = overlap. As a rough guide this overlap should amount to about $\frac{1}{4}$ in. per inch of average diameter of barrel up to 4 in., thus for a 3 in. barrel overlap would be $\frac{3}{4}$ in. and for a 4 in. barrel 1 in., above 4 in. this may be reduced to $\frac{7}{32}$ in. to $\frac{3}{16}$ in. per inch of diameter.

The next sketch shows how the joint is put together. Note that the edges of both cut portion and plain portion are feathered. The tags are hammered down and one or two rivets put through each tag and the uncut plate. Previously the mating surfaces should be thoroughly cleaned and coated with a thin paste of flux. Both edges should be annealed

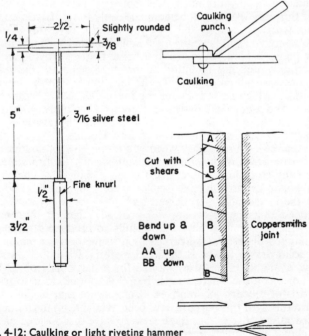

Fig. 4-12: Caulking or light riveting hammer

A baking tin makes an   Only sufficient rivets to
ideal brazing pan   hold things in place

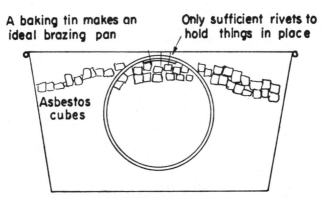

Asbestos
cubes

Fig. 4-13: Brazing set-up

before assembly and the whole joint well hammered to close the joints,
use a light hammer and .the flat face and only hammer sufficiently to
close the joints. Rivets should be countersunk on the *outside*.

When assembled and all fair, run around all the edges with some
additional flux.

The soldering will be greatly facilitated if the barrel is filled with
asbestos cubes and if additional asbestos cubes are built up around it,
as sketch, a large baking tin makes an excellent brazing hearth.

Make sure your heating apparatus is really adequate, more troubles
are caused by inadequate heating media than through anything else,
including improperly cleaned joints. Blowlamps are not the most
satisfactory of heat producers, but if you have to use one make sure,
(a) it has been thoroughly cleaned before you start and filled with *filtered*
paraffin of a good vaporising grade, nothing is more infuriating than
for the blowlamp to peter out at the critical moment, a habit which
seems inherent in the breed. Personally I infinitely prefer air-gas blow-
pipes of adequate capacity, either with a bellows of ample size, or better
with a low-pressure power driven blower. Oxy-acetylene is excellent
if you have learned the technique, but there is a lot to learn and it is all
too easy seriously to damage a job until you have mastered the art of
using the blowpipe; in any case the proportion of amateurs who own
such plant and know how to use it effectively, must be a very small
percentage of those who build, or want to build boilers*.

When your joint is made, it should be trimmed up with a file and if
the job has been well done it will hardly be visible on the outside, and it
will be as strong as the rest of the shell.

In erecting the boiler, the barrel longitudinal joint, however made,
should be positioned at about 45° in the upper sector, which side being
of no consequence. See sketch (Fig. 4-13).

* Since the above was written, bottled gas has come to the fore and is now not only
generally available, but there is also available a wide range of burners covering every
requirement, from the smallest to the largest. It has the advantage over coal gas or
North Sea gas that it requires no blowing air, being self sustaining and mixing.

The exact angle is, of course, not fussy. Personally for any boiler up to and including 5 in. gauge ($1\frac{1}{16}$ in. to 1 in. scale) I should use silver solder throughout, if carefully used its cost is far from prohibitive and in any case the more expensive grades need only be used for tubeplates and fitting bushes.

The facility with which it can be handled and the cleanliness and neatness of the joints it makes far outweigh its slight extra cost in my opinion. We are frequently told that brazing and bronze welding is simple and easy, but judging by the tragic bodges that one all too frequently sees, there are a lot of people who don't find them so. Many things are " easy " when you have all the facilities and have been doing them for half a lifetime, but the novice is apt to find them anything else but.

On the question of strength, silver soldering properly carried out will provide all the strength ever called for. The only place where brazing is necessary is on superheater headers, and even here, unless there are some most unusual conditions, B.6 will be perfectly satisfactory.

Where silver soldering (or, of course, brazing or bronze welding) is used rivets or screws need only be used in sufficient numbers to hold the joint together.

The " secret " of successful silver soldering is twofold, scrupulous cleanliness and thorough fluxing (and use the flux recommended by the makers of your solder) and ample heat in the place where it is wanted.

Where a second hard soldering operation has to be carried out on a part already partially hard soldered, the first soldering should be done with a high melting point solder, say, B6 or C4 (Johnson Matthey) and the subsequent operation with one of lower melting point such as " Easyflo " or " Easyflo " No. 2. An example of this occurs in an inner firebox where the joints are soldered before the tubes are inserted, the latter, of course, would be done with the lower melting point material.

Table VIII gives particulars of the characteristics and properties of the range of Messrs. Johnson Matthey's silver alloy solders and my acknowledgements are due to them for their courtesy in allowing me to publish them and their helpfulness with information bearing on the subject of the use of various types of their products for specific purposes.

This is not a treatise on hard soldering but before leaving the subject the following points are perhaps worth emphasising:

(1) Joints to be silver soldered should be made close fitting and *thoroughly cleaned* and fluxed before assembly. Only sufficient rivets need be used to firmly hold the parts together.

(2) The job to be operated upon should be surrounded as far as possible with asbestos cubes or asbestos millboard baffles so as to make it easier to concentrate the heat where it is wanted. Coke can be used but the fumes and heat resulting are most objectionable.

(3) Make sure your heating apparatus is master of the job and that it is in good working order *before* starting; if a blowlamp be quite sure it is well filled with paraffin. (Owing to the very considerable heat reflected from a big job the petrol or benzoline lamp is to be avoided.)

(4) Don't keep the heat on after the solder has run.

12. Above: Loco boiler with test pressure gauge in place

13. Right: Top view of loco boiler built by Martin Evans, with Belpaire firebox; note seating for safety valve and top-feed connections

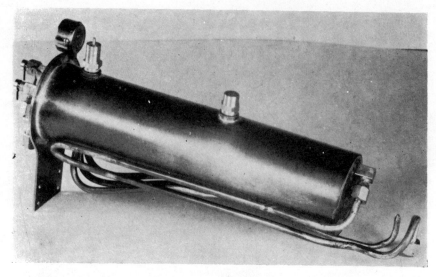

14. Above: "Smithies" type inner boiler. Note superheater and blower pipe and jet, made by Martin Evans

15. Below: Marine centre flue type boiler, with blowlamp

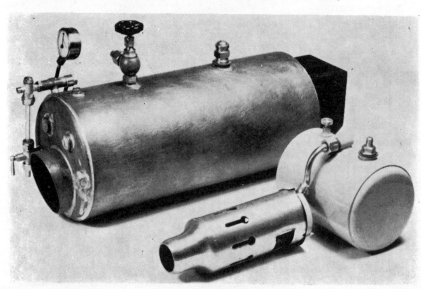

(5) Use plenty of flux, it is comparatively cheap.

(6) Don't quench the job in the pickle tank before it falls to black heat *in subdued light,* and keep well clear of splashes and fumes.

Riveting comes next for consideration. Rivets may be finished with countersunk heads, raised heads, round heads, conical heads, or pan heads, see sketch (Fig. 4-14).

The heads, as bought in model sizes, are either countersunk or round, flat headed rivets are also sold but are not suitable for model boiler work.

In full-size practice rivet holes were frequently punched, a practice which was cheap (and nasty) and in respectable boiler work today rivet holes are always drilled and frequently reamed as well.

For model work the holes should always be drilled; providing the correct size of drill is used, and providing that it is correctly ground, reaming is unnecessary. Both outer edges of the rivet holes should be slightly, very slightly, countersunk, just sufficient to remove the sharp edge and burrs should be removed from the mating faces of the joints, this is important in any case, and vital if a joint is to be made without solder, and mechanically caulked. Unless this is attended to the surfaces cannot lie in close contact with one another all along the joint, and it is essential that they should. The holes should be drilled so that the rivets are a good fit in them, rivets in oversize holes will never make a decent joint.

Of the heads shown in Fig. 4-14 the first three (left to right) are the most useful, the pan head is probably the strongest, but is not often used in boiler work (it was used largely on the outside plate frames of Kirtley's Midland engines with conspicuously successful results) and so may be disregarded. The raised head is rather stronger than the plain countersunk head and where it is covered by lagging is the simplest working proposition. Where scale appearance calls for round headed rivets, you can save yourself a lot of trouble by having the existing rivet head showing and doing your riveting on the inside; if, of course, you can get at it with the hammer !

This brings us to tools. These are few and simple but using the correct type for the job will simplify the work considerably.

Considering first hammers, I long ago came to making these myself. For reasons connected with the laws of inertia, riveting hammers should

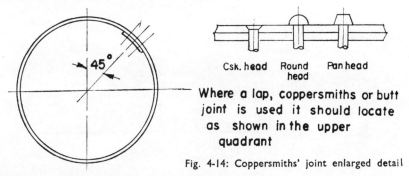

Csk. head   Round head   Pan head

Where a lap, coppersmiths or butt joint is used it should locate as shown in the upper quadrant

Fig. 4-14: Coppersmiths' joint enlarged detail

be made with long narrow heads. Fig. 4-12 shows such a hammer that I made for my own use, both head and handle are made from silver steel, and the handle is screwed tightly into the head with a fine thread, 40 t.p.i. in my case, and further secured with a taper pin.

Making the hammer is so obviously simple as to need no description, the ends should be made, one hemispherical and the other very *slightly* rounded on the face with its edge nicely radiused. The only tricky job is the tempering. The hammer should be made complete with its handle first, then taken to pieces and the head hardened, heat to cherry red, in subdued light, and plunge vertically into tepid water with a $\frac{1}{4}$ in. film of light oil floating on the surface, agitate vigorously. Remove and polish. The ends should be tempered to a light to medium straw. It is *possible* to temper both ends at once by heating the centre and watching the flow of colour, but it is a tricky job and I prefer to do them individually; the method is simple, get a sizeable potato and push the head into it for about half its length, apply a bunsen or spirit flame well back from the end and watch the colour, as soon as medium straw reaches the business end, quench out, reverse and repeat for the other end. The potato effectively prevents the heat spreading to the end *not* being operated upon. Use a *small* flame. *Don't* use a cooked potato !

The next tool is the Dolly, and it will take various forms according to the place in which it has to be used. The same structural principles apply to dollies as to hammer heads and the heavier they are, so long of course as they can be got where they are wanted, the better.

Where space below the rivet is unlimited a long dolly made from square mild steel is the goods, Fig. 4-15, $\frac{1}{2}$ in. square for $\frac{1}{16}$-$\frac{1}{32}$ in. rivets, $\frac{5}{8}$ in. square for $\frac{1}{8}$-$\frac{5}{32}$ in. rivets, and $\frac{3}{4}$ in. square for $\frac{3}{16}$-$\frac{1}{4}$ in. rivets (few model boiler makers will want anything larger). There are, of course, many situations in which the room available for the dolly is restricted, in fact this is more usually the case than otherwise, and the general answer is a heavy bar with inset small dollies, the bar should be of the heaviest section compatible with getting it into the required position. In use, of course, it will be held in the vice, and the overhang should be kept as short as the job in hand will allow.

The remaining tools needed are a drawing up punch and three snap punches. Here I must give credit to Mr. H. H. Groves for an excellent article on the principles and techniques of riveting using copper rivets,

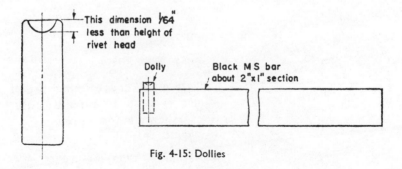

This dimension $\frac{1}{64}$" less than height of rivet head

Dolly   Black M S bar about 2"x1" section

Fig. 4-15: Dollies

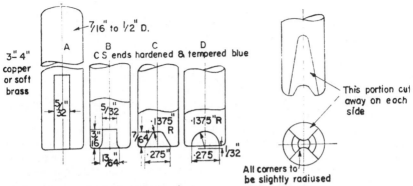

Drawing-up tool & rivet head sets
for hard copper sheets

Fig. 4-16: Punches and snaps. No. 5 is exactly the same as No. 4 but is *not* cut
away at the sides

which appeared in " Model Engineer " for April 6th, 1939, from which much of what follows is taken.

Fig. 4-16 shows the form of the punches required, their business ends only being shown. Depending upon the size of the rivets to be dealt with, the punches should be from $3\frac{1}{2}$ to 5 in. long and they are best made from silver steel (as, too, are the dollies and inserts in the bar dolly). The ends should be hardened and tempered dark straw, the ends to be hammered should be well rounded off and do not require hardening.

Punch No. 1, the " drawing-up tool," is required whether we are making countersunk, raised or round heads. Punches 2, 3, 4 and 5 are only required for round heads.

Punches 3 and 4 have their ends cut away as below.

Punch No. 5 is the same as Punch No. 4 but not cut away at the sides.

Let us first consider countersunk or raised head riveting and take as our example the riveting of the throatplate to the barrel. First we put our horizontal bar in the vice with the appropriate set in position and standing beyond the end of the vice jaws about $\frac{3}{4}$ in.

Copper being an extremely ductile metal there is almost certain to be a small degree of movement between the two parts being operated upon during the riveting process. For this reason the rivet holes should be drilled only in the throatplate spigot to begin with. Insert the barrel into the throatplate to the appropriate depth and check very carefully to make sure it is square in both vertical and horizontal planes, *this is of vital importance.* Now drill one hole through the barrel, say, on the top and insert a rivet (it is assumed, by the way, that the holes in the throatplate spigot are already countersunk) and resting the head in the dolly set, apply the drawing-up punch and then give it a few light blows with the round end of the riveting hammer; don't at this stage knock it right down, just sufficient to hold it in place.

Here it might be well to point out that in most riveting operations the help of an assistant to hold things in place, etc., is invaluable. Now check once more that the barrel is still square with the throatplate, and then put another rivet hole through it opposite the first one (180° from it) and proceed as for the first rivet. Again check for squareness and put holes through 90° from the rivets, and once more give a final check for squareness before inserting the rivets. If anything has shifted, don't attempt at this stage to correct the holes just drilled, square up and drill two more and again insert rivets and lightly knock down.

If after all this the job is not square you will either have been careless in your work or remarkably unfortunate.

You can now proceed to complete the riveting of the heads of your four rivets, using quite light blows and making sure you hit the *rivet* and not the metal around it. Work around the edges of the rivet and finish off with the flat end of the hammer. From here on the procedure is quite straightforward, keep interspacing holes and rivets, *don't* start from one of the rivets already finished and work straight on to the next. If you do, there is a likelihood of the natural stretch of the metal tending to cause the plates to open out from close contact as you proceed.

To show what is meant by this, consider the case of riveting the outer firebox wrapper to the throatplate and let us suppose you proceed to drill all the rivet holes through both plates, then starting, say, from the middle of the top edge you proceed to work on the rivets in succession down one side; after inserting three or four rivets you are likely to find that the succeeding holes are getting out of line, as indicated in Fig. 4-17.

Headed side

Fig. 4-17: Effect of stretching on rivet holes

Rivet heads as supplied

If this does occur the only cure is to open out the holes with a broach and fit larger rivets. Obviously this is laborious and most unsatisfactory and to be avoided, as it can be quite easily. The way to do this with complete certainty is to drill the outer wrapper only, start from top centre and drill and rivet at alternate holes, each side, until you come to the bottom edges, after which you can drill *all* the intermediate holes and then settle down to an orgy of riveting! It is quite likely that you will find the outer wrapper has stretched a little and overlaps the bottom edges of the throatplate, this is quite easily corrected with a milling file or a bastard file, but this is best left until last job, after backhead and foundation ring are fitted.

If you are coming new to this kind of work it is very strongly recommended that you should experiment with riveting together some scrap pieces of copper, before commencing on your actual boiler work; this is a cheap and certain way of gaining valuable experience, far more helpful than reams of instructions and will greatly assist you to make a satisfactory job of the boiler riveting proper.

Round-headed rivets require a different technique and what follows is directly attributable to Mr. Groves.

First of all the amount of protrusion of the rivet is of primary importance (with a countersunk headed rivet it is not so important as long as there is sufficient and a few trials will soon show you what is required, any excess can be trimmed off with a file after the rivet is knocked down [or up !], this, of course, is impossible with a round head). For a round head, the amount of rivet left standing proud when the two

plates are in close contact (an important point) should be $D \times \dfrac{8}{5}$

where D = diameter of rivet shank.

This a $\frac{1}{8}$ in. dia. rivet should protrude 0.20 in., a $\frac{5}{32}$ in. rivet $\frac{1}{4}$ in. and a $\frac{3}{16}$ in. rivet 0.30 in. These proportions will suit the punches shown in Fig. 4-16. Fig. 4-9 shows the successive stages of producing round heads.

Use drawing-up punch to close plates, follow with No. 2 punch, one smart blow, follow again with No. 3 with a series of light blows, working the punch round a little between each blow, repeat with exactly similar action with No. 4 and finish with one or two smart blows from No. 5. Once again a little preliminary practice with bits of scrap will be of great assistance in developing the requisite technique; once acquired it will become practically automatic. Whilst this type of riveting will normally cause much less stretching of the plates than will countersunk or raised head riveting, it is still advisable to adopt the same sequence of method as outlined for such riveting.

It may be thought that an undue amount of space has been devoted to this phase of construction, but it is so important and it is so easy to fall into trouble for the beginner that I consider it fully justified.

The last thing I would wish to do would be to exaggerate the difficulties, all of which can be overcome by the use of common sense (not always, alas, so " common "), care and patience.

Whilst I regard the suggestion that everything is easy when you know how as both misleading and untrue, it *is* certainly true that an understanding of the methods and principles involved is of primary importance. After that comes practice, and lots of it, and that is of at least equal importance.

One last point, don't forget before assembling and riveting a joint which is to be soft or silver soldered, thoroughly to clean the contacting surfaces first.

Caulking. This is a job which is unlikely to enter into the boilermaking of the vast majority of amateurs, unless really big boilers are in question. With a copper boiler I should never recommend it for plates less than $\frac{3}{16}$ in. thick, and even here would prefer soft solder caulking. Caulking is simply deforming the edge of the outer one of two plates which is in contact with the surface of inner plate. Fig. 4-12 will show what is meant.

The caulking tool is shown below and the method of application above. With copper, only quite light blows on the punch are required, anything more will be very apt to cause distortion of the plates.

With steel plates heavier blows are permissible and in fact necessary.

The technique is not difficult, but in any case few model boilermakers are likely ever to make use of it.

Drilling. Copper is easily the " stickiest " of the common metals. Special twist drills for copper are available, but unless there is a lot of this sort of work to be done, are hardly worth while. I prefer to use a well sharpened *straight fluted* drill with plenty of cutting oil, turps or milk as a lubricant, using a lower speed than you would for brass.

For holes over $\frac{1}{4}$ in. dia. it is better to drill a pilot hole and open out with a counterbore, as you are then assured of a truly circular hole of the correct size. Use a comparatively slow speed for the counterbore and plenty of lubricant.

If you try to drill a $\frac{1}{2}$ in. hole in a $\frac{1}{16}$ in. or $\frac{3}{32}$ in. plate, or a thicker one for that matter, you are quite likely to finish up with an oversize and anything but circular hole if you use an ordinary drill.

It is hardly necessary to point out that the pilot of the counterbore should be a good fit in the pilot hole; it sounds obvious, but it *has* been overlooked.

Tapping holes and threading rods. Copper is emphatically not a nice metal in or upon which to cut threads.

Your dies or taps* must be of first class quality and in first class condition, and you must use plenty of lubricant, I have found molybdenised grease dissolved in turps the most effective cutting medium for copper that I have tried, and I have tried a great many.

Copper, being a highly ductile metal, tends to deform and build up, as well as cut, when tap or die is applied, and for this reason tapping holes should be made a little *over* the nominal size and rods to be threaded kept a little below the nominal outside diameter. In the actual threading taps and dies should be eased back, taken out or off and cleaned frequently as the work proceeds, this is a nuisance and rather boring, but it is well worth while as it greatly helps in avoiding stripped threads.

Where stays are concerned I much prefer drawn phosphor bronze to copper, as apart from the fact that it is stronger, it takes a thread much better than does copper. Threading copper is one job that just can't be forced or hurried without almost certain trouble arising.

Generally it will be found that B.A. threads are preferable in or on copper to Whitworth form, and wherever possible their use is recommended.

Stay fitting. The fitting of longitudinal stays between the endplates of cylindrical boilers is a comparatively simple matter. Such stays, in fact all rod stays, should be threaded into *both* the plates they support. To do this directly involves one of two things, (a) the stay must be threaded for its whole length, or, (b) one end must have a larger diameter thread than the other *of the same pitch.* Both these methods are objectionable but fortunately there is a simple solution, which is shown in Fig. 4-18.

Occasionally hollow stays are required, more particularly in locomotive type boilers. When they are used, the cross-sectional area of the metal

---

* Whilst ground thread taps **are** expensive their cost is worthwhile if you have much threading to do in copper.

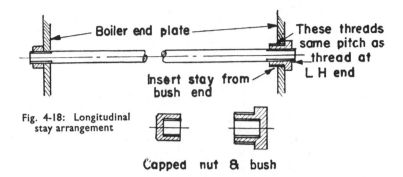

Fig. 4-18: Longitudinal
stay arrangement

Capped nut & bush

walls of the tube should be equal to the cross-sectional area of a solid
stay which would be used to carry a similar load, a reasonably heavy
gauge of tube should be used to allow for threading, and the area should
be calculated as if the *core* diameter of the thread were the outside
diameter of the tube, for reasons which will be obvious.

The locomotive type of boiler is the one which calls for the most
extensive and complicated system of staying of any boiler likely to interest
model boilermakers.

Most of this staying is required between the inner and outer fireboxes
In my opinion it is best carried out along the following lines. The outer
wrapper, throatplate and backhead should be marked out and drilled
for the stays before the inner firebox is put in place, but should *not* be
tapped.

When the assembly is complete and everything fixed either by riveting
or by hard soldering, the holes in the inner firebox should be drilled
using the holes already drilled in the outer casing as guides and taking
care that the drill is kept fair with the plates. The holes may then be
tapped using the special type of stay tap (a commercial article in the
model trade) having a pilot sufficiently long for the tap to pass through
the holes in both plates before it starts cutting; once again plenty of
lubricant and careful operation of the tap will pay dividends.

The stays should then be inserted, but before putting them in place,
thoroughly clean both inner and outer plates, obviously on their outer
faces (you can't very well get at the inner faces !).

The threads on the stays should be cut so that they are a reasonably
tight fit in the tapped holes, but don't overdo this and risk a broken or
jambed stay, as such is an awkward proposition to remedy.

Unless the firebox is large, large enough to operate inside with a small
hammer, the stays should project into the inner firebox an amount
equal to their own diameter and have a G.M. or Monel metal nut
screwed on to them tight up to the inner firebox plate; here again don't
overdo the tightening and pull the end of the stay off.

Where a stay comes on a curved surface, as it may do with a narrow
firebox at the point where the firebox bulges outwards, nuts should be
used with their mating faces slightly rounded as Fig. 4-19.

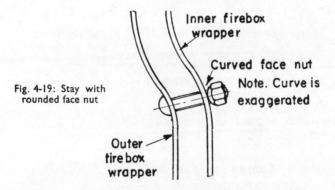

Fig. 4-19: Stay with rounded face nut

Inner firebox wrapper

Curved face nut
Note. Curve is exaggerated

Outer tire box wrapper

Where a firebox is large enough to allow of a small hammer being used inside it, the inner ends of the stays may be riveted over instead of nutted. If this is done they should be allowed to project only about half their outside diameter; the riveting should be done with a light hammer and the stay being riveted should be well backed up with a heavy dolly whilst the operation is in progress. This makes a neat job, but certainly calls for more skill than does the nutting method; care must be taken not to hit the plate around the stay-head, but only the latter. Generally this method is only to be recommended for those having a fairly wide experience of model boilermaking, and only then on fireboxes sufficiently large to allow of the hammer being manipulated with a reasonable degree of facility. Stay-heads (and nuts) are best caulked with a good grade of soft solder and this job should obviously not be attempted until *all* hard soldering, whether of the main boiler structure, or of fitting bushes, etc., has been completed. If the job is clean to start with, well fluxed, no great degree of heat is required and the solder will run where it is wanted like water. Don't apply the solder in excess, good lead-tin solder is expensive, and not only does excess application do no good whatever but it looks horrible and anything but workmanlike. Don't forget, immediately the job has cooled down, to give it a thorough washing inside and out, first with a weak solution of washing soda and then with plain warm water. By tackling this job immediately the remains of flux will be got rid of much more easily than if the job if left for a period.

Bushes for fittings and mountings. A practice not infrequently recommended is to make the backhead out of heavy gauge plate and tap the fitting holes directly in the plate. I regard this as a thoroughly unsatisfactory method. As has already been emphasised, copper is a bad metal for threading and even if a sound thread is produced the amount if thread is limited. The workmanlike way to do the job is to make bushes for the various fittings and silver-solder them into the appropriate places in the boiler shell.

The bushes should be made of drawn G.M. or P.B. rod and they should have a length of thread preferably equal to the outside diameter. There is no need for them to be clumsy and outsize. Things should be so arranged that the threaded portion of the fitting does not in any circumstances project beyond the inner end of the bush; if it does it is very liable to get a hard deposit of fur around the projecting threaded portion and to be found impossible, or at least very difficult to remove if and when this becomes necessary, and there are all sorts of reasons for such a situation to arise.

For larger boilers there is a great deal to be said for making the bushes plain bored and fitting them with studs, the fittings, of course, having suitably drilled flanges to match, but don't forget to make certain that you can get at the nuts to fix or remove the fitting. This may sound trite and obvious but it can be overlooked and cause much grief and consternation.

Bushes should be a good fit in their holes, and they and their surrounding metal should be thoroughly cleaned and fluxed before final assembling.

Fitting manholes and domes. Manholes are not often fitted to the average model boiler but they are quite useful for facilitating washing out. Unless scale appearance is of importance the type shown below in Fig. 4-20 is much to be preferred, it is easier to make, and much easier to make and keep pressure tight.

The hole and cover in the upper drawing are made oval to allow of the cover being turned through 90° for fitting or removal.

A reinforcing ring must be firmly riveted to the shell around the opening to compensate for the weakening of the shell occasioned by the cutting away of its substance for the hole. This reinforcing should be of material 25 per cent. thicker than the shell. A point to be borne in mind is that this ring in the flat will *not* be circular and will *not* have a circular hole in it, both hole and plate will be of elliptical form, and much the simplest way of finding the requisite shape is by the paper template method; it can be developed geometrically, but on general principles it is usually quicker and safer to use the template method.

This reinforcing ring is, of course, also required where a hole is cut out for a dome and don't forget that the dome flange itself will also be of elliptical shape.

The alternative method shown below is self-explanatory and calls for little comment. Here the adaptor fitting itself acts as a reinforcement ring and no separate ring is necessary. Useless space is at a premium, bolts are to be preferred to studs for fixing the cover to the adaptor flange, whichever is used, gunmetal, phosphor bronze or Monel metal is preferable to steel. Never on any account use steel or stainless studs or bolts in a copper boiler where they will be in contact with water and/or steam. If the joint in this case is properly made there should be no access of steam or water to the bolt or stud, but there is always the odd chance, and the use of non-ferrous bolts or studs cuts out all risks.

Wherever they can be used, domes are desirable fittings on a boiler. It is usual to cut out a hole in the shell equal in diameter to the inside diameter of the dome, which, as already pointed out, weakens the shell and calls for reinforcement. In most cases there is no necessity for this large hole and it is far preferable merely to drill a series of small holes in the shell in the area below the dome, the total area of such holes should be about 25 per cent. greater than that of all the steam supply pipes

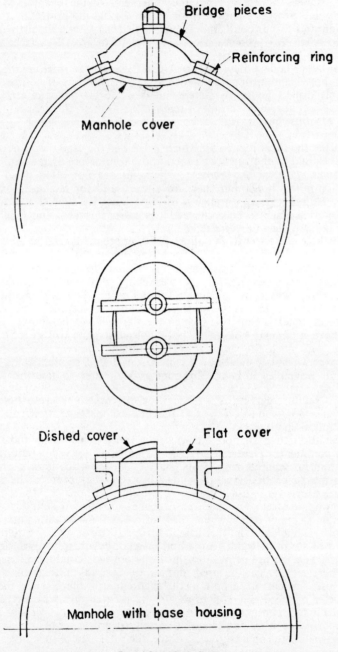

Fig. 4-20: Manholes

drawing off the dome. Where a regulator is fitted in the dome, a certain amount of thought and ingenuity will frequently allow of this same system being used. Where a regulator is fitted in a dome it is really essential that the dome itself should be removeable, or that its top at least should so be. This matter is dealt with in Chapter Six.

It is realised that this chapter is far from being as comprehensive as it might well be, but it is already nearly twice as long as any other and considerations of available space preclude its further extension. It is hoped at least that the main phases of construction have been covered with reasonable adequacy.

Foundation rings and firehole rings. Foundation rings can be made, (a) from G.M. castings; (b) from copper plate, or (c) from rectangular copper strip.

(a) is not recommended as, in my opinion, no form of casting in the actual structure of a boiler is desirable, though this objection as applied to a firehole or foundation ring is not serious.

(b) is a thoroughly satisfactory scheme but is expensive in material and calls for very accurate fitting, as also does (a);

(c) is probably all round the most satisfactory.

On first sight the statement about accurate fitting may be queried, but a glance at Fig. 4-21 will show just what is entailed. The shaded space has to be filled by the foundation ring, and it will be noted that there is an awkward double step at each corner. To get these four awkward corners all to fit at once in a single unit is obviously by no means an easy job.

Consequently it is strongly recommended that the ring be made in four separate pieces. As each piece can be fitted separately, this is a much simpler method. The end pieces should be fitted first and the side strips last to match. It hardly needs emphasising that the ends of the side strips should be in close contact with the end strips. To ensure this, it is best temporarily to remove the end strips before fitting the side strips, and to leave the side strips initially a little longer than the length to which they will be finished. I have seen it recommended that any interstices left can be blocked up with slivers of copper; of course, anyone is at liberty to do this, but they can hardly complain if a third party seeing such work classifies it as a bodger's job ! If a little care is exercised and no attempt is made to rush the job there won't be any interstices.

Much nonsense has been written anent the folly of making the foundation ring joint by riveting and soft solder caulking, it being alleged that such a joint will soon give trouble through leakage. This just is not true, if the ring is a decent fit to start with and a reasonable number of rivets are properly applied, this form of construction will remain bottle tight as long as the boiler will last. The boiler of the late James Crebbin's famous " Cosmo Bonsor " now 60 years old was made like this, and the foundation ring has never given a moment's trouble and is still bottle tight. The rivets should be carefully arranged, the dimensions and spacing being on the principles already laid down earlier in this chapter.

For firehole rings there are three methods:

(a) a similar arrangement to the foundation ring, though here it can always be made in a single unit;

(b) by shouldering down a thick piece of copper tube at each end, to fit the holes in the doorplate and backhead, leaving the untouched portion to act as a distance piece and brazing or silver soldering;

(c) by flanging the doorplate outwards and the backhead inwards and again fixing by brazing or silver soldering.

This latter is a method which I have evolved; I have never seen any reference to it, but it appears to be so obvious, that it would be surprising if nobody else had thought of it.

In my life I have seen far too many examples of inventions identical in principle and often in detail, coming from absolutely independent and unrelated sources, to be so foolish as to rush into print with claims to be the first in the field.

Put half a dozen competent engineers to solve a given problem independently and the chances are that two or three of the solutions arrived at will be so nearly identical as to make no matter. Steam engines and boilers have been made now for around 200 years, and genuine originality either in principle or detail is about as common as hen's teeth !

Fig. 4-21 shows the three methods, (a) being the one I should favour least. To carry out the forming of doorplate and backhead, the best method is by using dies and a fly-press, or in the absence of the latter, which few model engineers possess, a hefty vice. The dies are very simple turning and boring jobs, and if only one boiler is in question, one punch can be made to serve both backhead and doorplate, by forming the backhead first and then reducing the punch to suit the doorplate. Punch and dies can be made from mild steel, brass or at a

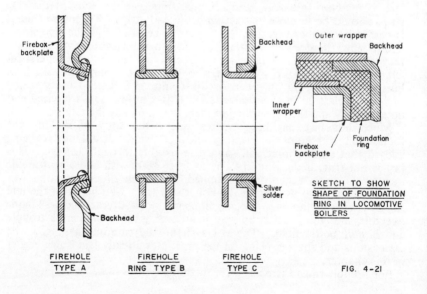

FIREHOLE
TYPE A

FIREHOLE
RING TYPE B

FIREHOLE
TYPE C

SKETCH TO SHOW
SHAPE OF FOUNDATION
RING IN LOCOMOTIVE
BOILERS

FIG. 4-21

pinch hard wood, such as oak or beech. Allowance for flanging will be on the principles already laid down earlier in this chapter, and, of course, both plates should be thoroughly annealed before forming. Both punch and die should be greased before operating; if wood is used for punch and die, use blacklead (graphite) as the lubricant and be sure to leave plenty of wood round the hole in the die to avoid any risk of splitting.

Method (c) has the definite advantage that there is no heavy body of metal around the firehole and further that it only involves one joint, whereas (a) or (b) both involve two joints. There is another method, not infrequently used in full-size practice, but this is not recommended for model work as it leaves a nasty narrow space for the accumulation scale and it also takes up a lot of room on the backhead, where space for fittings is always at something of a premium. Here again method (c) scores.

CHAPTER FIVE

Fuels and firing methods

THERE is a wide choice of fuels suitable for firing model boilers, and the use of any particular one of them will depend upon a number of factors.

Primarily fuels divide into gaseous, liquid and solid, referring to their state at normal atmospheric pressure and temperature. It is necessary to insert this remark as Calor gas, Botto gas, etc., come in liquid form in containers under pressure, but gasify as and when relieved of pressure.

Under the heading of gaseous fuels then, come coal gas and various "bottled" gases now on the market which have very large sales in country districts and for caravans, motor cruisers and yachts. There are of course many other gaseous fuels, such as blast furnace gas, producer gas, water gas, etc., but these are of no practical interest to the model boilermaker.

Under liquid fuels, come alcohol (methylated spirit), petrol, benzol, paraffin and heavy petroleum oil; the last being of no practical utility for our purpose. Under solid fuels, come wood, charcoal, coal and coke. Table II gives average calorific values for these fuels.

For a model to be worked indoors, gas firing is probably the best and simplest of all. It is instantly available, clean, if properly burnt odourless and very simply controlable, either by hand or by automatic apparatus, whilst it has the further advantage that simple and efficient burners suitable for most types of boiler are easily constructed by the amateur mechanic.

For regulation there is much to be said for a needle, adjustable in the jet orifice in combination with some simple means of varying the air supply.

A safe proportion for burner holes or slits, is to keep them slightly smaller in size than the thickness of the metal of the burner tube or plate, this reduces the likelihood of lighting back.

Fig. 5-1 shows a simple " bar " burner suitable for a horizontal externally fired boiler embodying a needle controlled jet and an air regulating

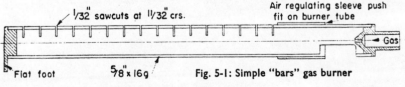

1/32" sawcuts at 11/32" crs.

Air regulating sleeve push fit on burner tube

Gas

Flat foot   5/8" x 16g   Fig. 5-1: Simple "bars" gas burner

device. When using gas in a closed, or partially closed, firebox, the adjustments to jet and air control should be made with the burner in its working situation, they are liable to be slightly different from those which will give the typical bunsen flame in the open air.

The foregoing remarks apply with equal force to the bottled gas family, but it should be realised that the ordinary coal gas burner is not suitable for use with them. The suppliers of these gases are always willing to give technical advice about burners for specific purposes. The burners used are identical in principle with coal gas burners, but differently proportioned as the bottled gas family, bulk for bulk have a much higher calorific value than has coal gas.

Gaseous fuels are absolutely ideal for auto control, which may be exercised either by pressure, as in the ordinary bulk water-containing boiler or by temperature where a " flash " or monotube boiler is concerned. In the former case, a diaphragm operated pressurestat is the best form of controller.

Fig. 5-2 shows the layout of a simple pressurestat. The action is as follows; steam from the boiler has direct access to the sealed chamber behind the flexible diaphragm, which is counter-loaded by the adjustable compression spring on its underside. When properly adjusted, on the

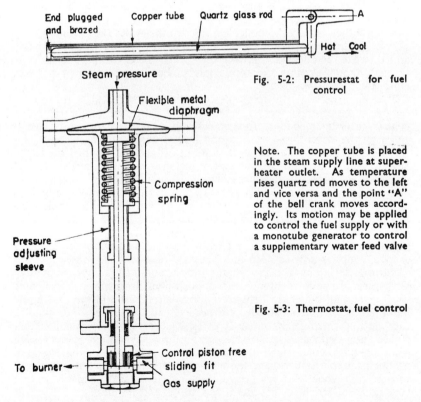

Fig. 5-2: Pressurestat for fuel control

Note. The copper tube is placed in the steam supply line at super-heater outlet. As temperature rises quartz rod moves to the left and vice versa and the point "A" of the bell crank moves accordingly. Its motion may be applied to control the fuel supply or with a monotube generator to control a supplementary water feed valve

Fig. 5-3: Thermostat, fuel control

desired pressure in the boiler being exceeded, the diaphragm is depressed and forces down the stem, which in turn closes, or tends to close the gas valve (it may, of course, equally well operate the jet needle on the burner itself where this is used).

Things must be so arranged that either (a) the gas supply cannot be completely cut off and the burner extinguished or (b) which generally speaking is the better proposition, a small pilot burner is arranged alongside the main burner with its supply by-passing the control valve, which serves to reignite the main burner when pressure falls and the gas supply is opened up again.

Shim brass, an easily obtainable commercial article, is excellent for diaphragms; for higher pressures suitable diaphragms are obtainable from the makers of Schafer type (diaphragm operated) pressure gauges. These are usually made with annular corrugations to increase their flexibility.

Both Stanley and White used this form of pressurestat on their steam cars and over a number of years and on some ten of these cars I never had the slightest trouble with them; they were absolutely reliable in action and appeared to maintain their adjustment indefinitely.

Fig. 5-3 shows in diagram form a simple thermostat for use with a " flash " boiler, here the steam supply passes around the thermostat, which, according as found constructionally most convenient, may be situated either within the boiler casing or outside it; the action is quite simple, as temperature rises the metallic element of the thermostat expands and this has the effect of allowing the end of the quartz rod to move to the left, thereby letting the spring loaded bell crank close, or partially close, the gas valve.

This again is, when properly designed and constructed, a thoroughly reliable piece of apparatus. Incidentally it can be used to control superheat in an ordinary boiler. In such case, the bell crank operates a needle valve on the water supply line to the boiler, which allows a small (very small!) quantity of water to go directly into the wet header of the superheater, or if no header, into the end of the superheater nearest the boiler, when the set temperature is exceeded.

Concluding these notes on gas firing, this is the ideal medium for indoor work where stationary engines are concerned. With bottled gas there are great possibilities for model locomotive firing, particularly for outdoor scenic railways. It provides considerable scope for the model locomotive fraternity to do a bit of experimenting and to get out of a groove, which is now so deep that you can't see over the top!

Turning to liquid fuels, by far the oldest, and still popular, is methylated spirit. In spite of many rather foolish jibes thrown at it, methylated spirit, for small boilers to be used indoors is the best and simplest liquid fuel there is. It is comparatively expensive, but it is clean and, handled with normal intelligence, safe. It gives a clear clean flame and neither makes, nor deposits soot. It requires ample ventilation, otherwise it will not burn completely, thus wasting its heating potentialities and producing unpleasant fumes, though to refer to these as " poison gas " will strike anyone who has been unfortunate enough to experience that very dreadful article at first hand, as fatuous and unfunny.

16. Above: Loco boiler, ready for fitting front tubeplate

17. Below: Group of fittings and mountings for test boiler

18. Above: Inner firebox with plate girder stays.   19. Below: Inner firebox wrapper with tubeplate

Methylated spirit can be used either in a simple wick lamp or in a vaporized condition, the latter being perhaps the most efficient method. In this latter case, for reliable working, a wick-fed pilot flame is almost essential.

Points to watch with spirit firing are to ensure that ample ventilation is available and that plenty of space is allowed between the top of the wick and the boiler barrel or firebox top, 1 in. should be regarded as an absolute minimum, $1\frac{1}{4}$ in. is better.

On the question of ventilation, efforts should be made to guide the incoming air into close proximity to the flames, unless this is done, the evaporative capacity and the efficiency of the boiler will both be reduced by the cooling effect of this air, particularly will this be the case with induced draught, as in a model exhausting up the chimney.

It is very rare indeed to find with spirit firing any attempt being made either to regulate the air supply or to guide it into the flame, but these are features very well worth the model engineer's attention and experiment. The accompanying Fig. 5-4 indicates lines along which experiment might well be carried out, almost certainly with profitable results.

The adjustable sliding shutters along the bottom edges of the case enable the air supply to be controlled, whilst the swinging dampers can be set to guide it into the flame of the lamp. The figure 5-5 shows an

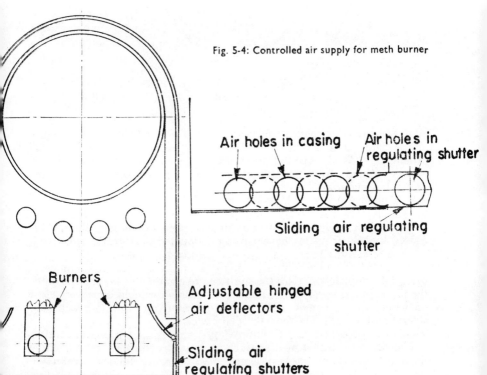

Fig. 5-4: Controlled air supply for meth burner

Air holes in casing

Air holes in regulating shutter

Sliding air regulating shutter

Burners

Adjustable hinged air deflectors

Sliding air regulating shutters

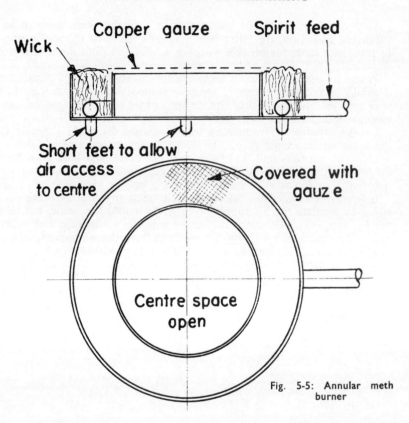

Wick

Copper gauze

Spirit feed

Short feet to allow
air access
to centre

Covered with
gauze

Centre space
open

Fig. 5-5: Annular meth
burner

annular form of burner in which a supply of air can come up the centre
of the flame, and it is a form which I can recommend from personal
experience. Wick type burners and their spirit supply tubes should
always be made from the lightest gauge tube available, brass being the
preferable material.

It is good practice to hard-solder a series of heat dissipating fins on
the supply tube just *outside* the firebox, see Fig. 5-6; this, in conjunction with light gauge construction, almost entirely eliminates the trouble
caused by heat from the burner being conducted back to the spirit container and causing vaporizing with its attendant troubles.

Fig. 5-7 shows a lamp of rather more elaborate construction than usual
designed completely to burn the spirit and to ensure that so far as possible,
the air required to support combustion, passes through, or in very close
proximity to the flames. This lamp is a semi-vaporising one and considerably more efficient than the plain wick type. In passing there is a
wide field for experiment in improving simple spirit burning apparatus.

The rate of burning of a spirit lamp is best controlled by regulating
the spirit supply by means of a needle valve, whilst for level regulation
the " bird bath " principle cannot be beaten.

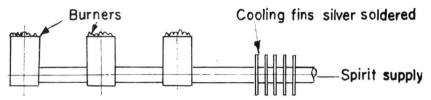

Fig. 5-6: Cooling fins on spirit supply pipe

Fig. 5-8 shows the complete layout of a plain, semi-vaporising trough burner, suitable for either stationary or marine work.

Where spirit is used for firing a locomotive type boiler, the blast should be kept quite soft and preferably some form of air regulation as already outlined should be incorporated. I am well aware that model locomotives have been fired " successfully " for years with plain wick burners, but I am sure that greatly improved results could be attained if air supply was carefully regulated and guided. The argument that such and such a thing " works " and, therefore, is best left alone and not interfered with by would-be improvers is, to me at least, one of the most fatuous and infuriating conceivable, if mankind had accepted that unprogressive attitude, we would still have been swinging around from trees by our tails. Every advance man has ever made has been due to those wicked and obstinate people who were not prepared to accept other folk's dicta, but had the audacity to think for themselves and to try, however unsuccessfully, to improve things, and so, and only so, will progress come in the future.

In constructing spirit lamps all parts of the burners themselves and any points near the burners should be silver soldered; tanks if well away from the burners may be soft soldered, but even here hard soldering is preferable.

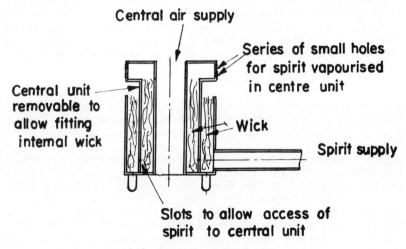

Fig. 5-7: Special spirit burner

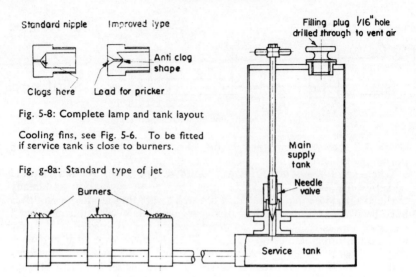

Standard nipple   Improved type

Anti clog shape

Clogs here   Lead for pricker

Filling plug ⅟16" hole drilled through to vent air

Main supply tank

Needle valve

Burners

Service   tank

Fig. 5-8: Complete lamp and tank layout

Cooling fins, see Fig. 5-6.   To be fitted if service tank is close to burners.

Fig. g-8a: Standard type of jet

It may be thought that too much space has been devoted to spirit firing, but for years this most useful fuel has been under a quite undeserved cloud; properly understood, handled and utilised in intelligently made apparatus, there are many situations in which there is nothing to beat it. For model scenic railway work, in or out of doors, it is hard to beat.

The late Mr. Victor Harrison's outdoor railway was an outstanding example of the latter kind of work, not with a single odd locomotive, but with a large and varied stud.   The same gentleman was equally successful with spirit firing for working model steamships, with exteriors very closely to scale.

Petrol and paraffin.   These two fuels are, for model boiler firing purposes, always burnt in apparatus basically similar and differing only in detail.   Petrol is very much more easily vaporized than is paraffin and is generally rather simpler to handle; it has less tendency to carbonise inside the vaporising elements, does not creep and smell when the burners are out of use for a time.

On the other hand it is not nearly so safe a fuel either to use or store.

Petrol should *always* be stored in a strong metal container with a screw stopper or cap, kept in a cool place and never opened or poured near a naked flame or hot stove, or whilst you are smoking.   This no doubt all sounds very trite and everybody knows it, or ought to: nevertheless many people get killed and more injured every year through neglecting these elementary rules.   Otherwise intelligent people will look into a petrol tank with a match—" to see if there is anything in it "— frequently they find out, but rarely live to tell anyone about it.   The remarks applying to petrol, by the way, can be taken as applying to benzole, too.

Petrol has a very high calorific value, the highest of all normal fuels, and thus is very popular as a fuel in the speedboat world, where the keeping down of weight is of primary importance.

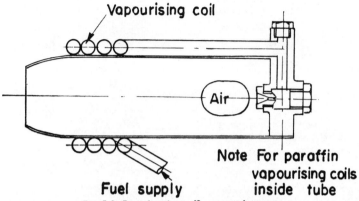

Fig. 5-9: Petrol and paraffin roarer burners

Paraffin has a somewhat lower calorific value than petrol but not sufficient to be of any practical importance.

It is an infinitely safer fuel, both to store and to use. The modern vaporizing paraffins are clean and efficient and in my opinion in nine cases out of ten, where the alternatives are petrol or paraffin, paraffin is preferable.

There are two types of burner suitable for using either fuel, the " roarer " truly so called because it does, and the " silent " which is very nearly so, In both the fuel is under air pressure.

The " roarer " is typified by the painter's or plumber's blowlamp in which a fine jet ejects the vaporized fuel through an open-ended tube, combustion taking place just inside the open outer end of this tube. The main difference in construction between a burner intended for petrol and one intended for paraffin lies in the vaporizer.

Fig. 5-9 shows a typical petrol burner. For paraffin, the vaporizing coils should be inside the burner tube. Petrol being much more easily vaporized than paraffin, it follows that the vaporizing tube does not require to be heated so much as does one to vaporize paraffin.

There are two means of regulating this type of burner. First by varying the pressure in the container, second by controlling the fuel supply. The first is only satisfactory within narrow limits. With the second method, control should be exercised on the vaporized fuel and not on the liquid, the latter is quite unsatisfactory. The best way of controlling the vapour is by means of a needle valve, the needle of which works in the jet orifice. Fig. 5-10 shows in enlarged detail such an arrangement. The taper of the regulating needle should be long and it should be so made that it is concentric in the jet orifice, to this end it is best so to construct it that its concentricity is dependent on plain turned and bored portions, not on a threaded portion, Fig. 5-10 includes this feature. A very prevalent trouble with blowlamps is the choking of the jet. The smaller sizes of the commercially made blowlamps rarely have vapour control and are almost universally fitted with jet nozzles made as Fig. 5-8. In

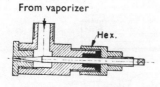

From vaporizer

Hex.

Note. Plain part of needle forms
guide to keep it concentric

Fig. 5-10: Needle jet control

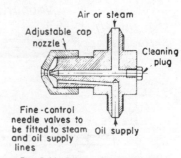

Air or steam

Adjustable cap
nozzle

Cleaning
plug

Fine-control
needle valves to
be fitted to steam   Oil supply
and oil supply
lines

Fig. 5-11: Palmer spray burner

consequence when the nozzle is cleared with a wire pricker any obstructing
particles fall into the enlarged portion of the nozzle and, more often than
not, soon find their way back into the jet orifice and block it once more.
The second sketch shows a form of jet nozzle which overcomes this
trouble almost completely. Here it will be seen that any obstructing
matter poked out by the pricker is most unlikely to find its way back
to the orifice.* Why this simple, cheap and effective remedy has never
(so far as I am aware) been commercially adopted it is hard to say;
probably our dear old pal, the practical man, had a great-grandad who
made the first blowlamp with a nozzle as shown in the first sketch, and
his descendants will go on doing so to the end of time; it " worked " so
that settled the matter !

For locomotive and locomotive-type boilers, vertical boilers and most
forms of water-tube boilers the silent type of burner is much to be
preferred. The essential constructional difference between the roarer
and silent types is that in the former ignition takes place at the outer
end of the mixing tube, usually in direct line with the jet, whereas in the
silent type, the jet delivers into a mixing tube, which itself discharges
into a burner chamber having on its upper surface a series of fine
sawcuts or small holes through which the combustive mixture excapes
and burns on top of the plate, exactly as in an ordinary domestic gas
ring. The vaporizer is placed above this plate and exposed to the burner
flames. In steam car and launch work it is usual where this form of
burner is used, to install a pilot burner, a small burner fed from a
separate pressure tank and usually situated under an enlarged part of
the main vaporizer; this pilot serves a double purpose, keeping the main
vaporizer hot when the main burner is cut down or extinguished by
the auto control, and re-igniting it when it " cuts in " again. These
pilot burners usually worked on petrol, as being more quickly started,
and in the days before specialised vaporizing paraffins cleaner and less
likely to cause carbonisation. In these days the obvious fuel for a pilot
is one of the commercial bottled gases. One of the main faults of the
silent regenerative type is " lighting back "; when used at high output
for a long period the burner plate may get hot enough to ignite the

---

* Incidentally the long taper greatly assists the end of the pricker wire to find its
proper destination.

gases in the burner chamber; alternatively, when cut down low, the speed of the gases through the sawcuts or holes, may fall below the speed of propagation of flame, and lighting back automatically happens. These troubles are almost completely curable by adopting a suitable form of construction.

In "Model Engineer" for May 5th, 1932, is a description of the Thorn steam car (or launch) boiler and burner. Incidentally, the boiler is one of the most ingenious I have ever come across but outside the scope of amateur construction. The burner in principle is exactly the same as that used for years by White & Stanley, Bolsover and many others, but it differs radically in the construction of the burner plate. It is made as Fig. 5-12.

This construction makes it practically impossible for the plate ever to become anything like sufficiently hot to ignite the gas in the mixing chamber whilst the long holes in the burner discs are too small to allow the propagation of flame within them. Discs of this form are used in the "Meker" bunsen burner, known to all familiar with chemical laboratory work, and are obtainable from the suppliers of laboratory equipment.

Where the silent type of burner is used it is highly desirable that it should be used in a closed firebox and all the air necessary for combustion taken in through the induction or mixing tube. This results in a far higher efficiency than can possibly be obtained with a burner working in an open firebox where inevitably large quantities of air are drawn in around it, a large proportion of which air by-passes the flames and merely serves to cool the boiler.

The closed firebox system usually requires that the burner should be worked at a fairly high pressure, White's used 60 lb. per sq. in. and Stanley's 120 lb. per sq. in. Burners of this type have to be designed to suit the job they have to do, and it is quite impossible to lay down rules for them. They are temperamental things and usually, unless one is exceptionally lucky, involve a lot of experimenting and adjusting to obtain optimum results, but this is not only most interesting, but most rewarding work, and once a burner of this type is right it is a most efficient and satisfactory piece of apparatus.

Those interested are strongly recommended to read Mr. Rodgers' excellent article on his 5 in. gauge 0-4-0 Contractor's locomotive fired on this principle which appeared, admirably illustrated, in the "M.E."

The type of burner in which the oil is atomised by a jet of steam is quite a useful one, though not very largely used amongst model engineers. The first of these to be applied to model work was described in the "M.E." by a Mr. Palmer nearly 60 years ago, it is simple in the extreme and, properly adjusted, highly efficient. Fig. 5-11 illustrates it.

Steam supply should be really dry, if possible superheated, and a finely adjustable needle valve should be used to control it. Such a burner is readily applicable to model boilers of many types, locomotive, horizontal and watertube, but not so suitable for vertical boilers. In the larger sizes it should not blow direct on to a firebox plate, but on to a firebrick lining, preferably beneath a reverbatory arch, see Fig. 5-12. Such a burner will lift its oil supply a few inches and is best set at a slightly higher level than the supply tank which makes flooding or fuel leakage impossible.

There are numerous variations of this type of burner and a number of different ones have been described in past issues of the " M.E.", one of the best and most adaptable of these was by Mr. Croall of the St. Albans M.E. Society in the " M.E."

Quite a number of burners are made in which the atomised spray is created by forcing the oil through a suitably designed nozzle at high pressure, but for model purposes it is almost impossible to make these nozzles small enough. The orifices required to pass the comparatively small amount of fuel needed for even quite large models are so tiny, that even if they can be made, it is practically impossible to prevent their being very quickly clogged and put out of action.

Some years ago Mr. Geo. Wildy and Messrs. Corderoy, Whatmore, Hayes and Shann carried out some interesting work on this problem in the S.M.E.E.'s workshop at Wanless Road, which is recorded in the Society's Journal for October, 1952, copies of which can, I believe, still be obtained from the Society's Librarian at 23, Wanless Road, London, S.E.24. For those interested in this type of burner this will be found of considerable value. Lune Valley type.

Lastly, in the field of liquid fuel apparatus, mention must be made of the carburetted air system, which has been used on the more modern types of steam car, notably by Doble.

In this system, what amounts to an ordinary simple carburettor is used, but, of course, as the natural draft through it would be quite useless

Fig. 5-12: Application to loco firebox of Palmer burner

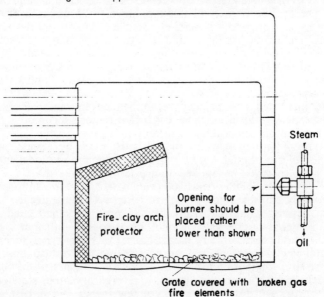

Steam

Fire- clay arch protector

Opening for burner should be placed rather lower than shown

Oil

Grate covered with broken gas fire elements

for the purpose, air is blown through it by a small high pressure fan. Ignition of the carburetted mixture is almost always done by a sparking plug, which, of course, necessitates a source of supply of electric current and a spark coil, together with auto switch gear, etc. Most of the modern automatic oil-fired domestic heaters work on this general principle, sometimes with the oil supply from a power-driven pump.

The system has its great attractions especially with auto control, but is hardly a practical proposition in anything other than really large models, or small power jobs. Some very interesting data and suggestions on this subject are to be found in Mr. Westbury's excellent little handbook " Flash Steam."

Finally we come to solid fuel, which, for locomotive fans in particular, has great attractions.

Whilst wood, charcoal, and coke can all be used, none of them are really nearly as satisfactory as is good steam coal; wood and charcoal burn very fast, and the former, if resinous, is apt to cause trouble on the firebars and in the flues, whilst coke is highly abrasive to plates and flues and its sulphur content is liable to damage copper.

Steam coal varies considerably in its heating capacity and characteristics. It is not always easy for the model engineer to get just what he wants in small quantities. Incidentally, one of the great advantages of belonging to a Model Engineering Society is the help that can always be obtained when problems of this sort arise.

On general points where solid fuel is to be used, arrange for a good sized firehole and door, for locomotives I prefer the drop-down door, followed by the double sliding door. When the former is used some means of admitting air when the door is closed should be incorporated. Such a door can be fitted with a butterfly air admission valve and an internal baffle plate to protect it from the direct heat of the fire; by this means air inlet can be regulated to a nicety.

Regarding grates, different types of coal require grates with differing air spaces, a good average proportion is to make spaces equal in width to bars; ideally the latter should be tapered, but this is not really necessary in the smaller sizes. For model purposes, bars made from one of the heat resisting steels are ideal, cast iron does not seem to be altogether satisfactory in grates of less than about 24 in. area. There should always be an air space between the outside bars and the inner firebox wrapper. In very small model locomotives bars may be as thin as $\frac{3}{32}$ in. but $\frac{1}{8}$ in. should generally be regarded as a desirable minimum. Wherever possible grates should be so constructed that the contents of the firebox can be dumped, making the grate in two sections often simplifies this, one section can be fixed (not, incidentally, in such a way that its dismantling for repair or replacement becomes difficult) and the other hinged the fire being dumped from the drop section first, the section raised and the fire on the fixed portion pushed on to it, and dumped in its turn. Some experimenting to attain the most satisfactory spacing of grate bars for the coal you are using is well worth while and fairly simple to carry out.

Rocking grates can be applied to locomotives of $3\frac{1}{2}$ in. gauge and upwards with advantage.

The fitting of a " Brick " arch and a deflector plate inside the firedoor of a locomotive boiler will not only improve combustion, but will do much (the arch, of course, not the deflector) to keep cinders and ashes out of the flues and smokebox. The deflector plate directs the air down into the fire when the firedoor is opened, instead of its rushing straight across into the tubes with deleterious effect on the steaming and superheat. Arches and deflectors are sometimes referred to as useless clutter, but in my experience and from personal observation of a great many model locomotives at work over the last 30 years that is exactly what they are not.* There is an oft-repeated saying that " experience teaches "; don't believe it ! Experience only teaches those who have receptive minds and are willing to learn and give up pre-conceived ideas when evidence shows them to be wrong.

Kipling says somewhere in one of his philosophical poems—" And the burnt fool's bandaged finger, goes wobbling back to the fire." Fig. 5-13 shows the arrangement of deflector plate and arch.

The former may be made from stainless steel sheet and should be so fixed that it can be removed from *outside* the firebox. The " brick " arch is best made from a piece of sheet iron or steel 16 to 12 s.w.g. perforated with a number of holes, say, $\frac{3}{16}$ in. to $\frac{3}{8}$ in. dia. and covered both sides with about $\frac{3}{16}$ in. to $\frac{5}{16}$ in. " Purimachos " or " Pyruma " allowed thoroughly to dry and then well baked before being put in place. The arch may rest on stay heads with slightly oversize nuts, or better a couple of arch tubes may be put into the firebox for it to rest upon. These, incidentally add valuable heating surface and improve the circulation in addition to their primary duty of supporting the arch. The sketch shows all the foregoing items. Note that the arch should be so made that when in place it leaves a small space, say, $\frac{1}{4}$ in. between itself and the firebox tubeplate, which will allow any fine ash which gets drawn over the top of the arch to be cleared.

Ashpans should always be fitted and so in my opinion should dampers at each end, a properly controlled air supply is of great assistance in attaining efficient combustion. Dampers fitted on centre pivots, to open as shown in sketch are I think the best, they tend to even out the air supply under the bars. The capacity of the ashpan should be as large as it can be made on a model locomotive, it is a nuisance, to say the least to have to keep raking it out. When passenger hauling the public for long continuous periods these things count, and one learns a lot of things that people who restrict their running ot a private track never even come up against.

Where available, the best material from which to make ashpans and dampers is undoubtedly stainless steel sheet. Ashpans made from mild steel or wrought iron rapidly deteriorate, especially if there is any dampness or leakage around, and the extra first cost of stainless steel (or iron) will be repaid many times over. Thought should be given to getting the ashes out of the ashpan, where possible a removeable pan is ideal, but in many cases this just cannot be arranged and some form of

---

* This applies to locomotives of $3\frac{1}{2}$ in. gauge and up; in the smaller sizes I have no personal experience of them.

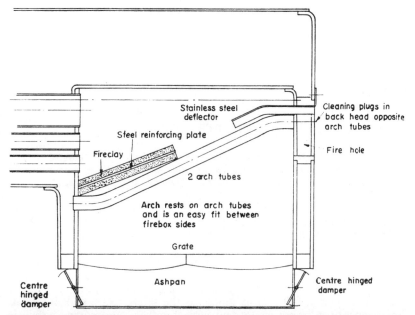

Fig. 5-13: Arrangement of boiler arch and deflector, arch tubes, dampers, etc

door has to be devised. A drop down hinged door is best where it can be fixed, otherwise a flat swinging shutter, on no account use a sliding door it will merely give trouble when you want to open it.

Much more might be said on this most vital matter of firing, but space forbids. It is a matter over which it is impossible to take too much care for it is the primary source of power and unless it is efficient you cannot have an efficient plant.

Many years ago, Archibald Sturrock, then Locomotive Superintendent of the G.N.R., stated that the power of a locomotive depended upon its ability to boil water; later H. A. Ivatt, another Locomotive Superintendent of the same railway, repeated this dictum and later still O. V. S. Bulleid, one of the most original and progressive locomotive men of the 20th century, brought the thing down to rock bottom by stating that it depended upon its ability to burn coal.

These dicta have been the subject of much " humorous " comment and ridicule. What the commentator overlooked was that the eminent gentlemen in question, in making their observations, assumed they were talking to normally intelligent people who did not need to be told the obvious truth that beyond the boiler there must be an efficient engine (and in the case of Bulleid, of course, an efficient boiler to convert as much of the heat of combustion into steam as possible). From the type of criticism referred to it is obvious that their assumptions were not of universal application.

CHAPTER SIX

Boiler mountings and fittings—Safety valves, water gauges, pressure gauges, stop valves, steam fountains, clack valves, blow-down valves, regulators, domes, steam collectors, separators

BOILER mountings and fittings might very well be made the subject matter for a complete handbook, and in a single chapter it will not be possible to do more than deal with general principles governing their design and application and to give a few detail drawings of some of the more important.

Unquestionably the most important fitting on any boiler (other than a monotube boiler), full size or model, is the safety valve, and due to its importance it is proposed to deal with it rather more comprehensively than it will be possible to do with other mountings and fittings. Safety valves are broadly divisible into two types, weight loaded and spring loaded; each of these subdivides into direct loaded and those in which the weight or spring operates upon a lever.

The weight-loaded lever safety valve is probably the oldest type of all, and the spring-loaded lever type is nearly as old. Whilst both these types, properly made, are thoroughly reliable, they are not ideal for model purposes, owing to the ease with which they can be tampered. This, of course, applies equally to full-size work and from quite early times it has been usual to insist on boilers having two safety valves, one of which should be of the " lock up " type and so insure against casual tampering and adjustment by unauthorised persons or ignorant old enginemen, a practice which in early days led to many fatal boiler explosions.

It is, of course, a comparatively simple matter to calculate the blowing-off pressure of a given weight lever safety valve, or to calculate the proportions of such a valve required to blow-off at a predetermined pressure and the formula is given below. This, of course applies to spring-loaded lever safety valves, too, but here there is the added complication that it is not easy to know just exactly how much tension is being applied by the spring.

It cannot be too strongly emphasised that *any type* of safety valve should be most carefully checked for its blowing-off pressure against a pressure gauge of known accuracy before it is put into use, and the same procedure should be followed whenever any repairs or adjustments are made.

A properly designed and made safety valve in good working order is a thoroughly reliable piece of apparatus, but unless it is correctly adjusted and kept in an efficient condition, it not only ceases to be a " safety " valve, but turns into a definite menace.

In Chapter One the effects of the Scale Law have been dealt with and their effect on the " weight " regulated type of safety valve mentioned.

Where an accurate scale model is in question it should not be overlooked that if a safety valve of the " weight-lever " or " deadweight " type is incorporated, the fact must be faced that if made to scale in every respect, the valve will lift at scale pressure, i.e., at a pressure relative to the working pressure of the original in the same proportion as the linear scale of the model; thus if prototype pressure was 120 lb. per sq. in. blow-off and the model is 1 in. to 1 ft. scale, its safety valve will lift at 10 lb. pressure.

This is a fact from which there is no escape and for that reason alone these types of valves should be avoided where external scale accuracy must be combined with good working qualities.

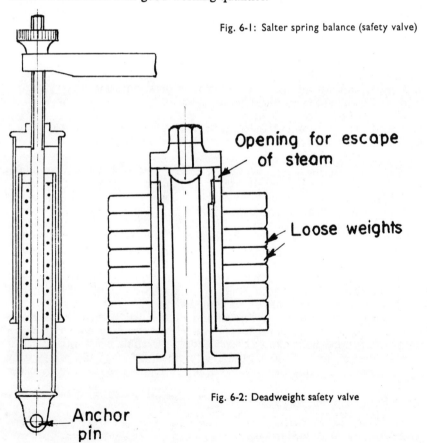

Fig. 6-1: Salter spring balance (safety valve)

Opening for escape of steam

Loose weights

Anchor pin

Fig. 6-2: Deadweight safety valve

The " deadweight " valve is simple and reliable and though it can be tampered with, tampering is less simple and more immediately obvious than it may be with the lever type.

Fig. 6-2 shows diagrammatically a deadweight safety valve. It consists of a centre column, communicating with the boiler, at the top of which is the valve. The outer weight carrying case is made a very free fit over the body of the valve and carries at its top end a central spigot with a pointed end which rests in the centre of the conical depression of the valve itself.

This outer case has a circular disc at the bottom, integral with it, which carries the weights, in full-size practice usually made of cast iron.

The calculations relating to its blowing-off pressure are very simple.

$$P = \frac{W}{aD}$$

where P = blowing-off pressure; aD = Area of valve
W = total weight of outer case and weights.

An important point to watch in its construction is to ensure that the point of contact between the pointed spigot and the valve itself is kept *below* the line of contact between valve and body; this, of course, applies to all forms of safety valve other than those using a ball for the actual valve.

FORMULA FOR WEIGHT LEVER VALVE

W = Weight in lb.
L = Distance from fulcrum of lever to cr of weight in in.
P = Pressure (above atmospheric) on valve.
A = Area of valve in sq. in.
Z = Distance from lever fulcrum to cr of valve.

$$W = P \times A \times \frac{Z}{L}$$

NOTE: Strictly the weight of the valve, etc., and of the lever should be taken into account, but for model purposes these can be ignored.

Fig. 6-1 shows the well-known Salter spring balance safety valve, for many years a great favourite with locomotive engineers, but now almost completely superseded by direct loaded valves. It is a good and reliable type, but involves a lot of work, some of it rather fiddling in the smaller sizes. Its use is not recommended for working models unless required for reasons of scale accuracy. In many of the locomotives of the Victorian era it was a most prominent feature, Johnson on the Midland and Stroudley on the L.B.S.C. Railway invariably used it.* The former always used an additional direct loaded valve.

In early days, before the invention of the dial type pressure gauge (Bourdon tube or diaphragm type) these safety valves were so arranged that the spring housings and lever ends were within reach of the driver and fireman, and it was customary for them to judge the pressure by the amount of force they had to apply to the end of the lever to cause the safety valve to blow off.

---

* The former right at the end of his long career with the Midland Railway, when he adopted the Belpaire firebox, fitted a Ramsbottom safety valve, with the addition of a direct spring-loaded lock-up valve.

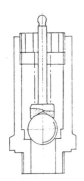

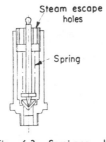

Steam escape holes

Spring

Fig. 6-3: Semi-pop, ball valve

Fig. 6-4: "Pop" safety valve enlarged valve and seating

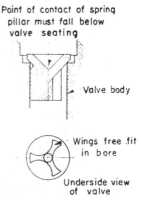

Point of contact of spring pillar must fall below valve seating

Valve body

Wings free fit in bore

Underside view of valve

For practical working model purposes the direct spring-loaded valve is undoubtedly the best proposition, either plain or " Pop." The " Pop " valve has come into very wide use for locomotive work all over the world; for the model maker it has one serious drawback, in that due to its violent action it is very apt to raise water and discharge it along with the steam; this is notably the case when there is little headroom above the water. There are two remedies for this: (a) suitably to mask the inlet from boiler to safety valve, and (b) to reduce the violence of the pop action.

Fig. 6-3 shows a " Pop " safety valve of simple type. The actual valve has a plain cylindrical upper portion and this falls below the edge of the recess, as indicated in detail. The area of the annular space between valve and valve body is somewhat smaller than the area of the hole through the valve. The action is as follows: when the valve lifts the released steam has not got a completely free escape, and acting on the enlarged upper part of the valve lifts it above the upper edge of the recess, the resultant escape is rapid, pressure in the boiler drops and can no longer support the valve against the spring and it shuts with promptitude.

The " pop " action can be controlled by a combination of dimensions, firstly by the area of the annulus between valve and recess, and, secondly, by the amount of " overlap " of the valve and recess, the smaller the former and the greater the latter the more violent will be the pop action.

Fig. 6-4 shows details of what may be called a semi-pop valve in which a ball is used in place of a wing valve. This is really halfway between a " Pop " valve and a plain valve and is a very sound working proposition.

The number of variations in safety valve design are legion, but the types enumerated will cover the needs of most practical model engineering work and space forbids a deeper delving into a very fascinating subject.

Water gauges. After an efficient safety valve, the fitting of a reliable water gauge ranks next in importance. For model purposes, the vast majority of boilers make use of a gauge embodying a glass tube, and if properly proportioned these are satisfactory and reliable. For higher pressures and larger models there is a lot to be said for the " flat glass-

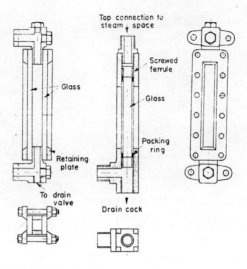

Fig. 6-5: Double-sided plate water gauge

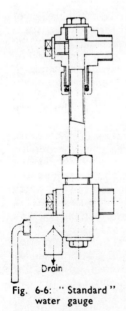

Fig. 6-6: " Standard "
water gauge

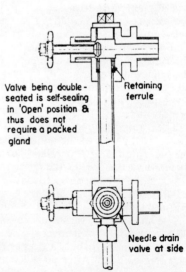

Fig. 6-7: Gauge with separate shut-off
valve,

window " type, single glass " Klinger," or double sided. One of the
latter type made by the writer is shown on plate 5, and a detail of this is
given in Fig. 6-5. No matter what type is chosen, a blow-down valve
should always be incorporated at the lower end.

Where a model is to be worked in public, and particularly does this
apply to model locomotives used at exhibitions, fêtes and on outdoor
tracks for public passenger hauling, shut-off valves should always be
fitted. Admittedly it is very rare for a gauge glass to burst, but occasionally this *does* occur, usually at a most inconvenient time. If shut-off
cocks or valves are fitted, the boiler can be stopped from blowing off
most of its contents over the surrounding landscape, and the necessity
for a hasty dropping or emergency extinguishing of the fire avoided,
whilst a new glass can be fitted quickly and in comfort.

In designing and making a small water gauge the most essential point
to watch is to ensure that the passages from the boiler through the
fittings have a clear way at least equal to, and preferably, in smaller
sizes, slightly larger than the internal bore of the glass tube. This, by the
way, is not a recent, let alone a new discovery, it has been recognised
by engineers for a hundred years at least, and it was, so far as I can
trace, first mentioned in " The Model Engineer " over fifty years ago by
the late Mr. L. M. G. Ferreira (January 20th, 1907, page 578). If this

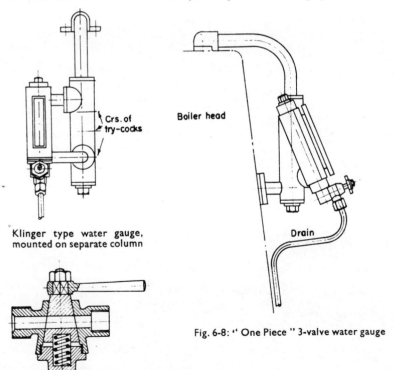

Crs. of
try-cocks

Boiler head

Klinger type water gauge,
mounted on separate column

Drain

Fig. 6-8: " One Piece " 3-valve water gauge

Spring loaded plug cock with inverted plug

principle is borne in mind, gauges with a glass as small as $\frac{5}{32}$ in. outside diameter are quite reliable, though where possible this figure should be increased to $\frac{3}{16}$ in. There is now available an excellent line in gauge glasses for models, having thin walls and with a narrow blue stripe fused along its length. When filled or partially filled with water this stripe is magnified in width, the tube acting as a cylindrical lens and thus providing a clear and unmistakable indication of the water level. Alternatively, if only plain glass tube is available, a length of polished stainless steel or nickel-silver rod, about half diameter of glass or rather less, can be fixed at the back of the glass and as close to it as possible. The effect is to make the water-filled space look as if it were filled with

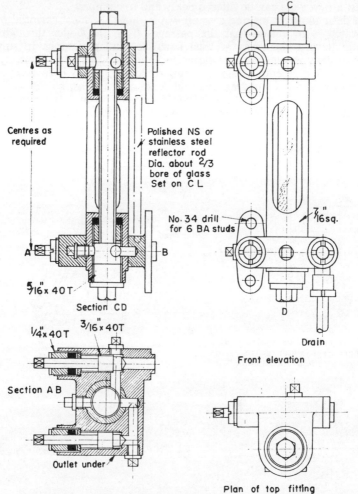

Fig. 6-9. Design for one piece body water gauge with shut-off valves and blowdown

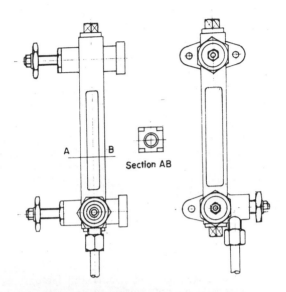

A B

Section AB

Fig. 6-10: Gauge with glass sealed by end-washers

mercury. The small gauge with shut-off valve seen in plate 2 is thus fitted. Tube water gauges are usually made with separate fittings top and bottom; dear old great Grandad made them that way and the practical(?) man has religiously followed suit ever since. This is, in a model, in my opinion, thoroughly bad practice, for under such circumstances, particularly where the fittings are screwed into the boiler shell, as they usually are, misalignment can all too easily occur, either in original assembly, or accidentally later. A design for such a gauge is included, but is not recommended. Fig. 6-6.

Far preferable is the one-piece body job, two versions of which are detailed in Figs. 6-8 and 6-9, one plain and one with shut-off valves. With this type there can be no misalignment and no external strains can fall on the glass which, moreover, is well protected from accidental damage.

When it comes to manufacture, there is probably no more work in the " one-piece-body " job than in making two separate fittings, and certainly less in assembling the finished article to the boiler. Finally, this type of gauge has been fitted to a large number of models of varying sizes over the last fifteen years with complete success.

Fig. 6-10 shows a gauge of this general type but with the glass sealed by end washers, invented by a colleague of mine over twenty years ago, which was in fact the inspiration of the one-piece-body types just dealt with. A number of these, too, have been used over the intervening years, again with complete success.

This " end holding " method has been condemned on the grounds: (a) that differential expansion (most impressive) will cause the glass to

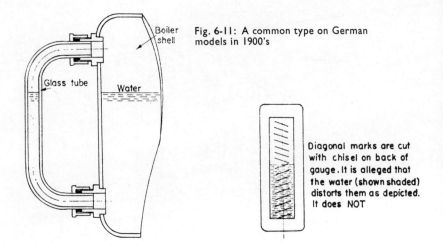

Fig. 6-11: A common type on German models in 1900's

Boiler shell

Glass tube   Water

Diagonal marks are cut with chisel on back of gauge. It is alleged that the water (shown shaded) distorts them as depicted. It does NOT

crack, and (b) that the packing rings will harden under heat and either crack the glass or cause leakage. The short and factual answer is that in *practice* this *theory* does not work out. Firstly, any differential expansion that takes place is of a very minute order indeed and in any case tends to *reduce* end pressure on the glass, secondly, there are a number of materials suitable for making the jointing rings which don't harden under heat but retain their initial flexibility. Anyhow, gauges embodying this principle have given years of trouble-free service, without ever a broken glass.

Just to nail the lid on the coffin of these allegations, as long ago as 1903 a well-known firm of boiler fitting and mounting manufacturers, still in business by the way, patented and introduced a metal protected gauge glass in which this end sealing method was the principal feature. Many hundreds of these were sold and used and I have seen a couple in use on a Lancashire boiler within the last three years. As these were made up to at least 21 in. long the " differential expansion " theory works out a bit weak for one, say, an inch long !

The lowest visible portion of the glass of any gauge should always be a little *above* the top of the firebox or whatever position marks the limit of safe level.

The fitting of the gauge on a separate water column is to be recommended wherever convenient, in passing the G.W.R. have used this principle from Daniel Gooch's time right through to the present day.* The lower connection to the water gauge should be kept away from areas of violent circulation otherwise false readings are all too likely to occur. Gauges, in use, should be blown down at frequent intervals, and if a glass becomes dirty and cannot be cleared by blowing down take it out and clean it immediately; sometimes the glass is actually chemically attacked by the

* Where a water column is used, it may well be fitted with a couple of level test cocks, this too is G.W.R. practice.

water and more or less frosted, in such a case the obvious and only cure is a new glass. Don't unduly tighten gland nuts or nipples, that leads directly to broken glasses. For ordinary pressures rings cut from suitable sized surgical quality rubber tubing are ideal as they will stand up to heat without hardening. Guards made from perspex are recommended, especially for gauges on engines which are going to be worked in public, they are simple to make and fit and do a lot to prevent serious damage in the rare event of a burst glass. Anyone has a right to risk his own skin, no one has any right to involve others in risk.

If the principles outlined in the foregoing are adhered to, then reliance can be placed on the water gauge, and this in conjunction with an efficient safety valve will ensure safe operation.

Check or non-return valves. These valves are an important group, broadly their purpose is to allow feedwater to enter the boiler, but at the same time prevent its getting out again, they are an essential ancillary to pumps and injectors. From the model engineering standpoint the ball valve has everything to recommend it and only this type will be dealt with. As with pump valves the lift of ball valves used as check valves should be restricted, a good average figure to keep in mind is a lift equal to one-eighth of the diameter of the hole sealed by the ball. Sometimes this type of valve is made in such a way that by means of a screw the valve may be positively held on its seating. This is not a practice to be recommended, much better is the arrangement shown in Fig. 6-12 in which a stop valve is included in the fitting in such a way that when it is closed the ball valve and its seating can be examined whilst the boiler is still under pressure.

Anyone who has had much experience of public passenger carrying model railway tracks will appreciate the value of this. In locomotive work the feed is put into the boiler in a variety of locations, through the backhead; the sides of the barrel, usually towards the front end; the bottom of the barrel, and the top of the barrel. The top feed is probably the best but it must be so arranged that the entering water falls clear of the flue tubes, and also that its " internals " can be removed for cleaning. Feed fittings, particularly any parts inside a boiler, are peculiarly prone to furring-up, with some types of feedwater quite rapidly, and arrangements must be made to counter this trouble. They should, therefore, be so constructed as to provide for easy dismantling and cleaning. Incidentally, for cleaning these items and boiler fittings in general, not forgetting injectors, soaking them in hot vinegar or lemon juice is effective. Hydrochloric acid is quicker acting, but in fittings, having

Fig. 6-12: Check valve with shut-off

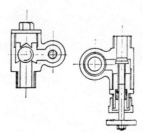

zinc in their alloy, there is a risk that the fittings themselves may be damaged. Where possible a flanged fitting, affixed by studs is preferable to one screwed into a bush, and except in very small sizes this method is strongly recommended. In this connection, with a copper boiler, fixing studs should never be of steel, not even stainless steel; use high grade drawn brass, gunmetal, phosphor bronze, or, best of all, Monel metal.

Fig. 6-13 shows a double top feed fitting for a locomotive boiler, or locomotive type boiler. As will be seen this provides for two separate feeds and has internal distributing pipes which throw the feeds out to the sides of the barrel, clear of the flue tubes. Mounted at the front end of the barrel, it can be inserted and removed through the enlarged flange hole for the main steampipe.

Where the clack valves are fitted on the backhead (or as sometimes designated, the boiler front) an internal pipe should be incorporated to convey the feed at least two-thirds of the way down the barrel towards the smokebox end, and it is essential that provision should be made for their easy removal; long internal feedpipes are absolute brutes for furring up. Never put the feed in at the bottom of the backhead, just above the foundation ring, this is a most unsatisfactory position.

The passage through a clack valve should be slightly larger than the bore of the pipe which feeds it. Stainless steel balls are preferable to bronze balls for check valves and the size of the ball relative to the hole it seals is important, a proportion of around 5 to 4 is about right; thus an $\frac{1}{8}$ in. hole requires a $\frac{5}{32}$ in. dia. ball, or a $\frac{7}{32}$ in. hole a $\frac{9}{32}$ in. ball (nearest available, strictly a ball 0.270 in. dia.).

In seating a ball, the usual instruction is to place it on its seat, and with a short piece of brass rod as a punch, to give it a clout. If you do this you may be lucky, or you may *not*, and if you are not, no amount of subsequent clouting will put things right. Unless the ball is struck truly on the axis line of the seating you will never get a true seat, and in consequence never a tight valve. To ensure proper seating it pays to make a temporary guide bush and a brass punch to fit it with a countersunk end, as sketch. Done this way you will get a tight seat every time.

The sketch shows the best form of seating for the ball, one much superior to the flat or worse still countersunk seatings, as sketches.

Fig. 6-13: Twin top feed fitting

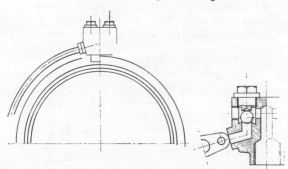

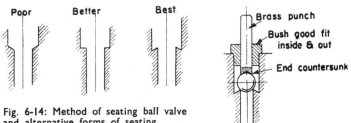

Fig. 6-14: Method of seating ball valve and alternative forms of seating

Either of these provide not only opportunity, but direct encouragement for bits of scale to lodge under the ball, the knife edge does not. This form was invented, so far as model engineering is concerned, by that great pioneer, the late Henry Greenly, well over forty years ago. Cutters to produce the appropriate contour can be made very simply from silver steel. (Fig. 6-14.)

Plug cocks have a bad reputation amongst model engineers, but this is really due more to faults in design and construction, and worse still, complete neglect in use, than to any inherent faults. Properly made of suitable materials to correct design, and properly maintained in service they will give little trouble. For some kinds of work they are to be preferred to screw down valves. To obtain satisfaction certain principles in design, manufacture and maintenance must be complied with.

To start with the taper of the plug is important, a taper of 1 in 9 to 1 in 9½ is satisfactory. Secondly, the plug and the body should always be made of different materials, say, G.M. for the body and a good grade of brass (not screw rod quality) for the plug. The plug should be ground into the body with a soft abrasive, on no account use emery or carborundum, which will bed in and form a permanent lap, powdered glass or rottenstone is as good as anything. Lastly, before assembly the plug should be well greased with graphite grease, and in use should be removed and regreased at fairly frequent intervals. If a plug cock starts to leak, take it out and regrind it immediately, it will *not* take up on its own, and if neglected may well seize up solid and cause permanent damage.

One other point relating to design, the holes through the body and through the plug should not exceed ½ in. dia. of plug on centre line of hole, this allows ample overlap when the cock is shut.

Stop valves and regulators. These can be divided into plug-cock, screw down, disc valve, slide valve and poppet valve types. Plug cocks are only suitable for small models and do not lend themselves well to sensitive regulation and we can leave it at that. Screw-down valves are almost always used on stationary and marine engine, whilst one of the three latter types are generally used on locomotive work, full size and model.

One thing applies to all of the family if an efficient working model is wanted, the passage through them when full open should never be less in area than that of the steampipe leading from regulator to engine. Any reciprocating steam engine of decent design and construction can only develop its full efficiency if the pressure in the steam chest closely approximates to that in the boiler. I am aware that in marine work it has been a not infrequent practice to generate steam at, say, 50 lb. higher pressure than required at the engine and to pass it through a reducing valve, but this is a quite special proposition connected with the efficiency of the steam raising plant, and in no way conflicts with the foregoing statement. Figs. 6-15 and 6-18 show two screw-down valves, one " straight through " and the other an angle valve; where it can be used the latter is the simpler constructional job. In larger sizes, say, ¼ in. bore and upwards the actual valve should be made separate from the operating stem, see sketch (Fig. 6-18).

Fig. 6-16 shows the well-known " Stroudley " type of regulator, but using a butterfly* disc instead of the more usual perforated type; by doing this much larger passages can be provided. If the valve and face are arranged as shown in Fig. 6-16 the ports in the regulator body will be opened in succession not all at once, thus giving much more sensitive regulation. Note particularly that with all types of disc valve, the centre portion of the disc and port face should be relieved.

The ports in fixed face are symmetrical. The blades on the moving valve are not.

This form of construction can be applied to any of this disc type of valve and it works most satisfactorily. Incidentally, so far as I can trace it was Greenly who first introduced the "disc-in-tube" type of regulator in model form, in his 1903 undertype engine design.

Properly made the disc type regulator is one of the very best, as it can be made very sensitive, it is easy to operate and has no tendency to

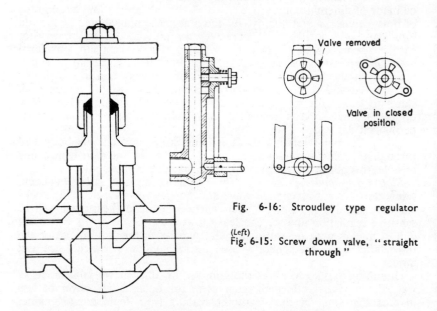

Valve removed

Valve in closed position

Fig. 6-16: Stroudley type regulator

(Left)
Fig. 6-15: Screw down valve, " straight through "

---

* A disc and port face with straight-sided ports.

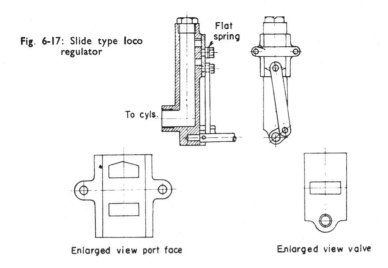

Fig. 6-17: Slide type loco regulator

Flat spring

To cyls.

Enlarged view port face   Enlarged view valve

stick. If desired a small " Vee " groove or notch can be filed in the edge of *A* to act as a pilot port.

Fig. 6-17 shows a slide valve regulator suitable for housing in the dome of a locomotive and is a type largely used in full-size practice. The drawing is self-explanatory and calls for no comment. Fig. 6-19 shows a type similar in principle suitable for installation in the smokebox and for operation by a " push and pull " lever. Incidentally, regulators, other than the poppet type are best kept out of the smokebox where possible.

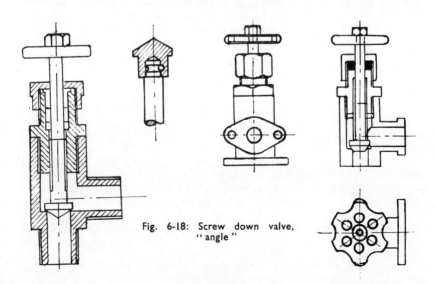

Fig. 6-18: Screw down valve, " angle "

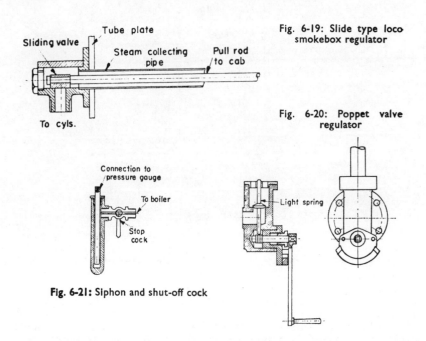

Fig. 6-19: Slide type loco smokebox regulator

Fig. 6-20: Poppet valve regulator

Fig. 6-21: Siphon and shut-off cock

Fig. 6-20 shows a simple poppet valve regulator, actually designed for the replacement boiler for the Greenly undertype engine. A point to bear in mind with a poppet valve is that when lifted to an amount equal to quarter of the diameter of the hole it closes, it is fully open and there is no point whatever in lifting it further. This is an excellent form of valve, well suited to high pressures and easily kept tight. It can be installed either inside or outside the boiler. By suitably designing the operating cam it can be made extremely sensitive. A point to watch is, so to design the cam that when fully opened there is no tendency for the steam pressure to make the valve close.

Pressure gauges. Whilst it is perfectly possible for the amateur to make his own pressure gauges, it is probable that very few will wish so to do, and it is not considered worth while to deal with their construction. Certain points should be observed. First instal the biggest gauge you can, by which I mean up to 2 in. or $2\frac{1}{2}$ in. dia., the larger the gauge the more accurate it is likely to be and remain. Secondly, a gauge should always read to at least 50 per cent. greater pressure than the working pressure, better 75 per cent. or 100 per cent. plus.

Choose a gauge having as open a scale as you can find, centre handed gauges give a much more open scale than the excentric type, but cannot normally be obtained less than $1\frac{1}{2}$ in. dia. Plate 22 shows a centre handed (and accurate) gauge with a dial only $\frac{3}{8}$ in. dia., made by an old friend of mine, Mr. Karl Meyer, but this is *genuine* watchmaking work, outside the capabilities of all but an exceptional few.

Lastly, gauges used for steam must always be protected from the direct access of steam to " the works " by means of a siphon, this may be in the form of a coiled or looped tube, in which the steam condenses before reaching the gauge, the pressure being transmitted by a column of water.

Fig. 6-21 shows a very neat form of combined siphon and shut-off cock, simple and effective. A well made gauge, protected by an efficient siphon and operated well within its maximum indication range is a reliable instrument, but it is desirable to check a new gauge, either against one of known accuracy, or on a deadweight tester. If you have any reason to suspect that a gauge is not recording accurately, test it at once. A method of testing under *steam* using a thermometer in place of a pressure gauge is referred to in Chapter Seven and can be used as a substitute when no other gauge or testing apparatus is available.

Domes. A steam dome of ample capacity is of considerable value in a model boiler for the collection of dry steam. Practically no modern locomotives have domes of such a size that when reduced to model proportions they are of any practical use, but many of the older types had domes of ample proportions. Generally they can be applied to stationary and marine type boilers with advantage.

In most cases there is no need whatever in a model boiler to cut out a hole in the shell equal in size to the internal bore of the dome, such a hole considerably weakens the shell and should always have a substantial stiffening ring say 25 per cent. thicker than the shell closely rivetted to the inside. It is far better to leave the shell intact and in the portion covered by the dome to drill a number of small holes having a combined area say 25 per cent. in excess of the area of the steampipe leading from the dome.

Domes are best built up from copper tube and plate, silver-soldered or brazed. Figs. 6-22, 6-23 show two examples, one a " solid " dome intended for use where it does not house a regulator and the other a dismountable dome for use where the regulator is housed within it.

Collector Pipes. Where a dome cannot be fitted, steam should always be collected from the highest part of the boiler. In locomotive work the raised firebox, particularly the raised Belpaire type is most helpful. A perforated pipe, set close to the boiler shell (or firebox top) is the best all round method for a domeless model. The total area of the perforations in a collector pipe should exceed the area of the pipe itself by from 15 to 25 per cent., and needless to say the perforations should be kept along the top line of the pipe.

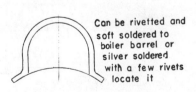

Fig. 6-22: " Solid " dome

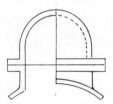

Fig. 6-23: " Dismantling " dome

Generally every effort should be made to ensure that steam is collected from the highest part of the boiler, and if top feeds are used, no collection of steam should be made anywhere near them.*

Steam Fountains. These are most useful fittings, not only on locomotive boilers (they are almost universal on modern full sized locomotives) but on most other types as well. Their use reduces the number of holes that are required in the boiler shell and is of considerable assistance in effecting neat and tidy pipe layouts. In the larger sizes the header should have a main isolating valve, so that if necessary packing and adjustment of the various distributing valves can be carried out with the boiler in steam, but in the smaller sizes this may safely be omitted. A small steam fountain with four distributing valves for injector, blower, vacuum ejector and steam brake, plus a spring loaded chain operated whistle valve are commonly used in locomotives.

Steam Separators. These are useful fittings in stationary and marine work, particularly where there is some distance between boiler stop valve and engine. They are very simple in principle and depend for their action on the fact that water carried along with the steam has much more inertia than the steam and in consequence cannot follow a sudden change of direction. The sketch herewith indicates the principle. There are many ways of carrying this principle into effect, but the one shown is about as simple and effective as any. Note that when in use they should be drained at regular intervals, if they become waterlogged, they will obviously cease to function. The body should be, say, three times the bore of the steampipe in diameter and six to eight times steampipe diameter in depth, inside. (Fig. 7-2.)

The whole fitting should be well lagged as it exposes considerable area and loses a lot of its value unless it is well insulated. It is hardly necessary to point out that the steam pipes leading to and from it should also be well lagged. The fitting should be installed as close to the engine cylinder or cylinders as it conveniently can be.

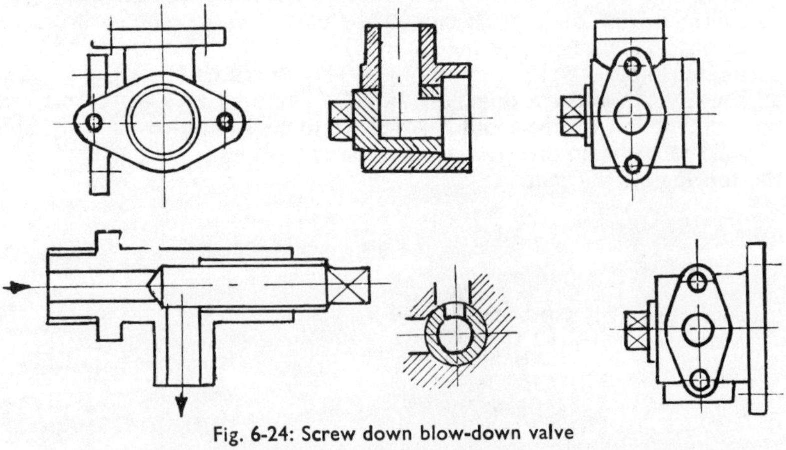

Fig. 6-24: Screw down blow-down valve

---

* Steam should not be collected in proximity to the safety valve(s).

Blow-down Valves. A blow-down valve should be fitted to any boiler, however small; if used regularly they help to keep the boiler free from mud and scale. In full size practice they are frequently of either the plug cock or swinging disc type, but for working models neither of these is recommended; the plug cock is particularly apt to get corroded and frozen unless very carefully maintained and lubricated. For practical model work the plain screw-down valve is far and away the best proposition. The sketch, Fig. 6-24, shows the type of valve and, in anything but the smallest sizes, it should be attached to the boiler by a flanged joint; if screwed into a tapped bush, the chances are that if after a few months working, you want to take it out, it will be hard to move, and the threads will be found well and truly furred up. The clear bore should be made as large, within reason, as possible; even in the smallest sizes it should not be less than $\frac{1}{8}$ in. clear bore, on a 5 in. gauge locomotive it should not be less than $\frac{1}{4}$ in. bore. The blow-down valve should always be used when shutting down after a run; with a locomotive boiler working perhaps for several hours at a stretch a short blow-down every hour or so is advantageous, more especially if you are in a hard water district. Blowing down should never be done violently, open slightly only at first and let pressure drop gradually, if blowing right down, don't open fully until pressure is down to 10 lb. per sq. in. or less.

Wash-out and Cleaning Plugs. These small accessories should be fitted in locomotive and vertical boilers at foundation ring level, in such positions that cleaning rods can be got in to clear out sediment which may (and probably will!) have collected.

The threads used should not be too fine and here again the plugs should be as large as convenient, $\frac{3}{16}$ in. should be regarded as an absolute minimum and the brass pipe thread (26 t.p.i. for *all* sizes) is a good one to use. The plugs should have a taper thread and should be made of gunmetal or phosphor-bronze with good size square heads.

They should be well coated with graphite grease before screwing into place, and they should not be long enough to protrude beyond the inner face of the bush.

CHAPTER SEVEN

Testing Model Boilers

NO model boiler, or for that matter *any* form of pressure-containing vessel, should ever be put to work without first having been pressure tested and found to be structurally sound.

In full size a hydraulic test pressure of $1\frac{1}{2}$ times the working pressure is generally used, in model work twice the working pressure is more usual, and may for all ordinary purposes be taken as satisfactory. With a steam test, a pressure 10 per cent. in excess of the working pressure is sufficient.

There is not only no good purpose served by carrying a hydraulic test beyond twice the working pressure, but permanent harm may easily be done. Not infrequently, in reading descriptions of working models, one finds it stated that a boiler, intended to work at around 80 lb. sq. in., has been tested hydraulically to 300 lb. or more " . . . and was absolutely tight and showed no signs of distortion." If a boiler is intended to be worked at 80 lb per sq. in. and is properly designed for this pressure, it is just asking for trouble to test it to nearly four times its normal load. It may well remain tight and show no *visible* sign of stress, but it is highly probable that this excessive test pressure may have stressed some part or parts beyond their elastic limit, and that at some later time, it or they, may well fail even below the working pressure of the boiler, with disastrous results.

The usual method of carrying out a hydraulic test of a model boiler is by means of a hand pump. A hand test pump I made some years ago, proved to be capable of working up to 1,000 lb. per sq. in. or more. This pump was really more elaborate than it need be but was designed for the maximum convenience in use.

A reliable pressure gauge of known accuracy is a necessary piece of equipment for boiler testing, and it should preferably read to *twice the test pressure*, certainly to not less than $1\frac{1}{2}$ times the test pressure. Within reason the larger the dial of the gauge the better; good pressure gauges can often be acquired at very moderate prices at many of the surplus stores. Before being used for test purposes a gauge should always be tested against another of known accuracy, or on a dead-weight gauge testing piece of apparatus. If the gauge being tested is not accurate, a correcting chart should be made up on the lines indicated on the next page.

Correct Pressure Master Gauge	Pressure Gauge Reading Test Gauge	To Correct
10 p.s.i.	8	Add 2
20 „	20	—
30 „	33	Subtract 3
50 „	55	„ 5
80 „	90	„ 10

When carrying out a hydraulic test it is important that the boiler should be absolutely filled with water and that no free air whatever should remain in it. Where a boiler has a dome with some form of outlet at the top, it is fairly simple to get rid of the air, but whatever the conditions, before applying pressure, be quite sure you have got all the air out. Obviously all orifices such as bushes for fittings, washout holes, manholes, etc., must be plugged or made good. Once the air is out of the boiler and all joints are tight the pressure will rise with each stroke of the pump, always presuming there are no bad leaks. On no account should the pressure be raised too quickly, pump up to 10 lb. examine all round for leaks or signs of distortion (hardly likely to appear in the early stages unless there is some radical constructional fault) then put up to 20 lb. and repeat examination. Carry on raising pressure say 10 lb. at a time and examining carefully between each raise, minor leaks should be marked with chalk for attention later.

Assuming all goes well, when the test pressure is reached maintain it steady for half an hour. After this pressure can be released, but *don't* do this with a rush, release pressure gradually and the whole structure of the boiler can settle down to an unstressed condition comfortably. This is of particular importance with boilers of complicated structure and large numbers of stays such as locomotive types or Scotch marine boilers with water-surrounded combustion chambers.

There is another method of carrying out a hydraulic test, by which the use of a pump is eliminated. This is to fill the boiler absolutely full of water, getting rid of all air before finally sealing the last orifice. When filled *very gently heat* with a bunsen burner, or in small sizes a spirit burner, watch the pressure gauge closely and proceed in pressure stages exactly as described for the pump method. Water is, for practical purposes, incompressible, and once the air in the boiler is got rid of, a quite small raising of the temperature will result in a rapid rise in pressure. Be sure to proceed carefully, too rapid or too intense an application of heat, or heating for too long a period may easily send the pressure rocketting up to an undesirable extent. There is no actual danger in this, at least no danger to life or limb, as if anything fails, all that happens is a quick leak and an immediate drop in pressure to zero, but one does not want to run the risk of damaging, maybe beyond repair, a boiler into the construction of which much valuable material and labour has gone. *Festina lente* is in this connection an excellent motto.

It is hardly necessary to point out that a hydraulic test should *always* precede a steam test, and that the latter should on no account be proceeded with until the former has been satisfactorily carried out. There is not much to be said about the steam test, but here again, go steady with steam raising and don't carry your test to a pressure in excess of working pressure plus 10 per cent. It is very rare for a boiler which has stood up satisfactorily to the hydraulic test to give trouble with its steam test. Don't forget that for a steam test, the safety valves will either have to be set temporarily to blow off at the required higher pressure, or removed and their sockets temporarily plugged. Don't on any account, if the former procedure is followed, forget to re-set the safety valves to their correct blowing-off pressure before putting the boiler to work.

One more point concerns the pressure gauge, for the steam test this must have an efficient siphon fitting to ensure that hot steam cannot get to the Bourdon tube, if it does it is liable to upset the correct reading and damage the gauge permanently. This matter of siphons is dealt with in the chapter on Boiler Mountings and Fittings.

Finally when the test is concluded, let the pressure drop naturally, don't open the blow-down valve suddenly and let the pressure down with a rush. Above all, when carrying out a steam test, be careful, there is no danger if a failure occurs, even a severe rupture, with a hydraulic test; a steam test is an entirely different matter and a failure of any magnitude can be very dangerous. Of course, this does not apply to minor weeps, but to failure of joints, stays, or actual rupture of plates.

Do not get the idea from the foregoing that the steam test is dangerous; if it follows a properly conducted hydraulic test, made at not more than twice the working pressure, and normal caution and commonsense are used, there is no danger whatever, but steam and water at high temperature and pressure have great potential energy and should always be treated accordingly.

As mentioned previously, it is possible to use an accurately graduated thermometer in place of a pressure gauge for the *steam* test. A study of Table I shows that as steam pressure is increased so also is its temperatue, though not in direct ratio. Thus, to take some instances:

Gauge Pressure	Temperature °F.
25 p.s.i.	267
50 „	297
75 „	320
100 „	338
125 „	353
150 „	366

a range which will cover most of the requirements of the average model boilermaker. Table I gives the figures over a wider range.

All that is necessary is an accurate straight stemmed mercury thermometer covering the range of temperature required. A margin should be allowed at the upper end, but this need not be large it will be noted, for example that the increase in temperature when raising pressure from 125 lb. to 150 lb. is only 13° F. The more open the scale of the thermometer the better.

Obviously the thermometer bulb must *not* be subjected to pressure, and a special fitting must be made up to screw into one of the mounting bushes on the boiler. The sketch shows such a fitting which can be made from gunmetal or from good quality brass. (Fig. 7-1.)

20. Above: Loco boiler with wide Belpaire firebox and sloping throatplate and backhead, built by Mr. Alec Farmer

21. Below: Horizontal internally fired boiler and vaporing spirit lamp

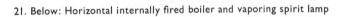

22. Left: Backhead for a 1¼ in. gauge Pacific loco built by the late Karl Meyer. Note the one piece body water gauge and the centre hand pressure gauge, which is only ½ in. dia. over the casing and was made by Mr. Meyer. This picture shows that even with such a tiny loco, it is perfectly possible to obtain a good layout and proportionate fittings

23. Below: Complete firebox with girder roof stays, backhead, front tubeplate and throatplate for 1¾ in. scale narrow gauge model loco. The throatplate flange fits *outside* the barrel

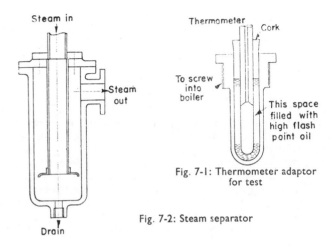

Fig. 7-1: Thermometer adaptor
for test

Fig. 7-2: Steam separator

Given an accurate thermometer, this method gives extremely reliable results, and incidentally it can be used to check the accuracy of the pressure gauge.

Wherever possible, when carrying out a steam test all the boiler mountings and fittings should be in place, so that they can be tested at the same time as the boiler itself.

The importance of careful and thorough testing cannot be too highly emphasised. It does not take long and is really very little trouble, whilst it is very interesting work and there is a lot of satisfaction in seeing your designing and constructive efforts performing " according to plan."

Boiler testing is not a thing that should be done once and then forgotten, with a boiler that is frequently worked it should be done once a year, and where a boiler is out of use for any lengthy period a test (hydraulic) should be carried out before it is put to work again. On no account accept a second-hand boiler without first having a proper hydraulic pressure test carried out upon it. Probably 19 times out of 20 such tests are perfectly satisfactory, but the odd time a weakness will be shown up and it is this odd chance against which it is, in the interests of common-sense and safety, vital to take precautions. It is no use saying: " Oh I'll take a chance," that is a fool thing to do with your own safety, and near criminal with other folk's safety. This applies with particular force to *steel* boilers.

There is another form of boiler testing which is rarely carried out, more's the pity; i.e. evaporative capacity and efficiency. Such tests are of the greatest interest, they involve quite a lot of work in carrying out, if the results obtained are to be reliable and of any real value, but to the intelligent model engineer with an enquiring mind they are of great potential value and there is an appalling lack of reliable information on the whole subject, as there is on far too many other phases of model engineering.

It is not proposed to deal with the subject in any detail, as it is probably not of sufficient general interest to warrant the space it would occupy, but a few general hints may be given. First and foremost, don't set out to " prove " some pre-conceived idea, if you do you will almost certainly succeed in deceiving yourself, even if you don't deceive anyone else. The very essence of worthwhile experimenting is to attempt to find out facts, to see what happens in a given set of circumstances. Secondly always get one or more independent observers to assist you, check and take notes of results. Thirdly, never alter more than one condition at a time between any two experiments. Fourthly, repeat each experiment under any given set of conditions several times, and if any particular result varies widely from the average, ignore it, if they all vary widely there is something badly amiss with your controls. In evaporative tests, two things are most important: (*a*) to make sure that all feedwater goes into the boiler, a leaky pump or injector can put up the apparent evaporative capacity of the boiler under test to astronomical proportions!; (*b*) make sure that the steam delivered is really dry steam; here again water carried over with the steam merely flatters the result and entirely discounts its value. A simple extractor or separator is of great help in this connection.

This sort of work is thoroughly worth while, but if it is to be of any value at all, it must be carried out with meticulous attention to detail and scrupulous honesty of observation. Self-deception is all too easy, and frequently completely unintentional, hence the absolute necessity for independent observation. The sketch herewith, Fig. 7-2, shows a simple and quite reasonably effective form of separator. This should be placed as close as possible to the boiler and should be lagged as effectively as possible.* In use it should be drained at frequent intervals, obviously if it is allowed to become waterlogged it will very quickly cease, not only to act as a separator, but will provide a reservoir from which the entering steam can actually pick up additional water and carry it over.

---

* This matter of placing the separator close to the boiler applies only to evaporative tests, as pointed out earlier, for working purposes it should be placed close to the *engine*.

CHAPTER EIGHT

Tube proportions, spacing and layout, superheaters and feed-water heaters

THE sizes of flue and water tubes, relative to the boilers to which they are applied, are of great importance. In what follows on flue sizes and later in regard to the proportions of flue tube super-heaters relative to the flues in which they are housed, I am almost entirely indebted to the work of Mr. C. M. Keiller, the only man I know who has got down to brass tacks and evolved a set of principles, not just of particular application to a special case, but of general application to boilers of all sizes, work which has permanently removed guesswork, trial and error and intuition(?) completely from this particular field.

Before considering individual flue tube proportions, something should be said about the total area of gas-passage for the products of combustion in relation to firegrate areas. This proportion will vary more or less directly with the available draught, i.e. the stronger the draught the smaller may be the total gas passage provided.

Under all normal conditions the model locomotive boiler provides the strongest draft. Forced draft with a closed stokehold or fan induced draft is extremely rarely met with in models; in the 60 odd years of the existence of the *Model Engineer* there have probably been well under a dozen working models, described in its pages, so provided. Thus for all practical purposes this type of arrangement may be disregarded.

That is not to say that there is not here an excellent field for the model engineer who likes to do his own thinking and enjoys experimenting, there certainly is, and one too which holds out great and interesting possibilities.

In a locomotive boiler (for locomotive work) the gas area through the tubes should not be less than 1/7th (one seventh) of the grate area and may without detriment be as high as 1/6th (one sixth). For what may be described as more or less natural draft boilers 1/4th (one fourth) is a good all round figure.

It is not suggested for a moment that departure from these figures is fraught with dire and inevitable disaster, they are merely given as a general guide. Where few large tubes are used there is less resistance to gas-flow than where numerous small tubes are used, where tubes are necessarily long, proportionally larger cross sectional area should be provided. Like everything else in engineering there is scope for com-promise and the exercise of reasoning power and common sense. After all, " theory " is only another name for " thinking " and one presumes that even the most dyed-in-the-wool " practical men " occasionally think, or do they ?

Looking at another angle of this matter it must not be forgotten that the area of the bore of a tube varies as the square of its diameter, whilst its surface area varies directly as the diameter. Thus a $\frac{1}{2}$ in. bore tube has a cross-sectional area of 0.196 sq. in. and an internal circumference of 1.57 in. whilst a 1 in. bore tube has a cross-sectional area of 0.785 sq. in. and a circumference of 3.14 in., four times the area, but only twice the circumference of the $\frac{1}{2}$ in. tube. Thus it is obvious that for a given size of tubeplate we can get far more heating surface with $\frac{1}{2}$ in. tubes than with 1 in. tubes, but not so much gas passage area. Once again, it is a matter for compromise and judgment.

It is usual to calculate heating surface on the " wetted area," i.e. on the outside area of flue tubes and on the inside area of watertubes or superheater elements. Now as to proportions of flue tubes; Mr. Keiller's investigations led him to produce the following very simple formula:
Where $D = dia.$ of flue (external dia.)
$\qquad L = length$ between tubeplates
$$\frac{L}{D^2} = 60 \ to \ 80.$$

To take one or two practical examples we have a locomotive boiler 10 in. long between tubeplates, what sized tubes should we use. We will take the mean of the two figures given above, 70

so $\dfrac{10}{D^2} = 70$ and $D^2 \dfrac{10}{70}$ $\qquad D^2 = 0\cdot14$

$$\text{and } D = 0\cdot378$$

which for all practical purposes can be taken as $\frac{3}{8}$ in. dia. tubes.

Suppose, on the other hand we have on hand a stock of $\frac{7}{16}$ in. dia. tubes and want to know the optimum length between tubeplates to suit them.

Once again we will take the mean figure of 70. $\frac{7}{16}{}^2 = 0\cdot192$ so we have $\dfrac{L}{\cdot192} = 70$ and $L = 70 \times \cdot192 = 13\cdot4$ in. so we can space our tube-

plates $13\frac{1}{2}$ in. apart. Again, remember we have taken the mean figure of 70 so we have a margin of something better than 14 per cent. either way for our length, i.e. it will comply with the rule if our tubeplates are anything between $11\frac{3}{4}$ in. and $15\frac{1}{4}$ in. apart. However, the figure of 70 for general purposes is an excellent one at which to aim.

When it comes to tube spacing a very simple and safe rule to follow is to allow a " bridge " between tube holes of not less than $\frac{1}{4}$ of the o.s. diameter of the tube, thus with $\frac{3}{8}$ in. dia. tubes, the space between any two should not be less than $\frac{3}{32}$ in. Put another way, the measurement centre to centre of tubes should not less than o.s. diameter of tube + 25 per cent. Thus for a $\frac{3}{8}$ in. tube $\frac{3}{8}$ in. + $\frac{3}{32}$ in. = $\frac{15}{32}$ in. crs. min. Where there is ample space in the tubeplate for the number of tubes required, this figure can with advantage be increased up to $D + 33$ per cent. or even $D + 40$ per cent. This allows of stronger bridges, always the weakest part of the plate and one that in full size practice frequently gives trouble through cracking. This is especially liable to occur where the tube

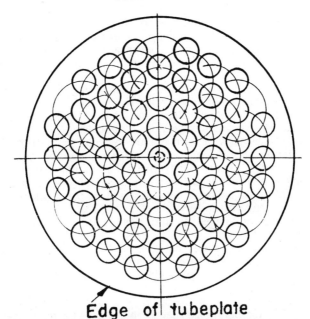

Edge of tubeplate

Fig. 8-1: Tube layout for circular tube plates

Fig. 8-2:   Tube layout Scotch marine

expander is used with more enthusiasm than skill.

There are numerous ways of setting out tubes. For vertical boilers the method indicated by Fig. 8-1 is the simplest and most satisfactory and one which gets the greatest number of tubes of a given size and pitch, in a given space or area.

This method is, of course, equally applicable to tubeplates of other than circular shape, and taken all round is probably the best and simplest method of setting out. It will be noted that where the tubes are horizontal this method can be applied in two ways, (a) as shown, in which the tubes lie in vertical rows and (b) by turning the diagram through 90° when the rows become horizontal. Method (a) is preferable as it gives a freer path for the escaping steam bubbles.

Fig. 8-2 shows a setting out in vertical rows, almost always adopted in Scotch marine boilers. For model purposes this presents no advantages and fewer tubes can be got into a given area; it is not recommended unless it is desired to produce an accurate scale model of a type of boiler in which it is used.

There is, of course, nothing binding about having the tubes absolutely symmetrically spaced, cases frequently arise where departure from strict symmetry is, if not absolutely necessary, at least desirable. Such cases frequently occur with locomotive firebox tubeplates.

Where it becomes desirable or necessary to depart from strict adherance to given centre distance throughout, two things should be borne in mind. Firstly the " bridge " between any two tubes should never be reduced below $\frac{1}{4}$ of the tube diameter; with the exception that where ordinary tubes are adjacent to enlarged superheater flues the " bridge " may be $\frac{1}{8}$ of the smaller tube diameter without undue risk. Secondly a general symmetry should be arrived at and every endeavour made to avoid " wide open spaces."

Whilst increasing the spaces between tubes reduces the number that can be placed in any given tubeplate, and thus the heating surface, on the other hand it makes for freer circulation and easier escape for the steam bubbles. Once again it is a case of compromise and judgment.

Don't place tubes too near the edges of a tubeplate or too close to a boiler barrel. In the first place they should not be nearer to the edge of the tubeplate than twice the thickness of the plate, see Fig. 8-3,

$$A = 2B \text{ minimum}$$

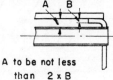

Fig. 8-3: Position of tube in tubeplate

A to be not less than 2 x B

and in the second place not nearer the boiler barrel than $\frac{1}{2}$ diameter of tube or flue. The proportions of water tubes vary to a much greater degree than do those of flue tubes, generally it can be said that the more rapid the circulation, the longer a tube may be relative to its diameter, or put another way, the smaller may be its diameter relative to its length.

It must always be borne in mind that in model boilers the skin friction of the tubes is very much greater than it is with full-sized boilers, due to the fact already pointed out, that whilst the surface, either inner or outer, of the tube varies directly as the diameter its cross sectional area varies as the square of the diameter.

An accurate scale model of a Yarrow boiler would be a hopeless working proposition for this reason alone, quite apart from others.

With the popular Smithies watertube locomotive boiler, the tubes are frequently made much too small, one not infrequently sees tubes 9 in. or 10 in. long and only $\frac{3}{16}$ in outside diameter. As a rough guide it is suggested that such tubes should have a bore to length ratio never greater than 1 to 50, 1 to 40 would be better. Any reduction in nominal heating surface caused through using fewer larger tubes is far more than compensated by the greatly improved circulation resulting. With this type of boiler it is both possible and practical to provide washout plugs in the " downcomer " or backhead (where a wet backhead is used) opposite each tube, thus providing excellent facilities for cleaning out the tubes; this is particularly desirable where hard water has to be used. For boilers of the type with rising spiral tubes such as the Lune Valley or Bolsover Express, the tubes can be much longer relative to their diameter, in some cases over 200 times bore, but these are exceptions. Very generally a figure of length = 50 times bore is a pretty sound maximum figure to keep in mind.

With both flue and water tubes, particularly with flue tubes, light gauges should be used, as this assists heat transmission; $\frac{3}{8}$ in. flue tubes may be of 20 to 24 S.W.G., $\frac{7}{16}$ in. and $\frac{1}{2}$ in. tubes 20–22 S.W.G., $\frac{5}{8}$ in. tubes 20 S.W.G., again as a general guide. An additional advantage of using a light gauge for water tubes is the larger water passage provided for a given outside diameter.

If tubes are to be fixed by expanding, then a somewhat heavier gauge than would otherwise be necessary should be used. For tubes up to $\frac{7}{16}$ in. o.s. diameter required to be expanded, the thickness should not be less than 21 S.W.G. (0·032 in.), $\frac{1}{2}$ in. to $\frac{5}{8}$ in. 19 S.W.G. (0·040 in.), and $\frac{3}{4}$ in. to 1 in. 17 S.W.G. (0·056 in.). " Field " tubes can be used successfully having a widely varying range of proportions.

Normally the outer tube should not be less than $\frac{3}{8}$ in. o.s. diameter as a minimum, preferably $\frac{7}{16}$ in. The inner tube should have an internal cross sectional area equal to or slightly in excess of the area of the annulus between its own outer diameter and the bore of the outer tube, thus more or less equalising the rate of flow throughout its travel. Where " Field " tubes are used at an angle of 45° or less from the horizontal the inner tube may be replaced by a simple strip of thin sheet metal fitting the diameter of the tube and stopping short at a distance from the lower end equal to about half the diameter of the tube. When the tube is fixed the diaphragm should lie in a horizontal plane.

As indicated the diaphragm should project a little way beyond the inner end of the tube. Field tubes in the right situation are highly efficient; in model work they find their most suitable application in boilers fired by gas, spirit or oil.

In full size work they have been extensively used for small vertical boilers, notably for fire-engine work as previously mentioned, but they have also been used in large water-tube boilers, the best known of which is probably the " Niclausse," at one time largely used in the French Navy.

Where cross tubes are used in a horizontal flue or firebox, as in the popular (but thermally most inefficient) single flue marine boiler, they should always be fixed either vertically or at an angle of at least 15° from the horizontal, adjacent tubes should not be placed in line with one another, whilst the spacing between adjacent tubes should not be less than $\frac{1}{2}$ tube diameter. In full size practice the tubes used in a Cornish Lancashire or Galloway boiler are set vertical or nearly so and are tapered with the small diameter at the lower end.

Speaking generally, water tubes, especially when directly exposed to the flames, are very rapid steam raisers. Where they are of considerable length relative to the grate, it is usually desirable to introduce baffle plates to guide the hot gases through a sinuous path, and to make sure that all the tube surface gets its fair share of heat, hot gases are like human beings, lazy, left to themselves they will take the easiest and most direct course to the chimney, and if this is allowed, it may well result in some of the tube surface receiving little heat and so doing little work.

Superheaters. Probably the type of superheater best known to most model engineers is the locomotive flue tube superheater, and it can be said straight away that properly designed and made it is a most efficient job, much more so that the smokebox coil or gridiron or hairpin type. However, there are several things to be said about this. Firstly there are certain relative proportions as between the size of the flues and the size of the elements they contain which must be adhered to within fairly close limits if efficient results are to be attained. Secondly, it must be realised that the skin friction of the comparatively long elements and particularly of the return-bends is quite considerable and in consequence ample total cross sectional area must be allowed through the elements, otherwise there will be a most undesirable drop of pressure between the " wet " " hot " headers. Where these conditions are met and where also, the whole steam supply line from regulator port to steam chest is of ample cross sectional area and without restrictions or right angled bends, and where the exhaust line is equally well designed and carried out, " scale " or " overscale " sized cylinders in model locomotives to attain reasonable power at speed are not only quite unnecessary, but from a thermal efficiency point of view thoroughly undesirable. Anyone who is interested in this aspect is recommended to read an article by Mr. C. M. Keiller in the *Model Engineer* for June 15th 1938, dealing in detail with the performance and proportions of a model locomotive of his own build $2\frac{1}{2}$ in. gauge $\frac{1}{2}$ in. to 1 ft. scale and having cylinders only $\frac{1}{2}$ in. bore by 1 in. stroke. The facts disclosed in that article amply confirm the foregoing remarks not on a basis of theory but on a basis of factual highly successful performance. It may be taken as a good all-round figure for this sort of work that the cross sectional area of the bore of the main steam pipe for a two cylinder locomotive should be $= \frac{D^2}{16}$ where $D =$ cylinder bore, whilst the total cross-sectional area through the superheater elements should be from 25 per cent.-33 per cent. greater than this.

I have a very strong suspicion that many alleged " superheaters " on model locomotives at the best are only steam driers, and at the worst, merely an extension of the evaporative surface.

Turning for a moment to smokebox superheaters, whilst not nearly so effective as a properly designed and made flue-tube superheater, they are certainly better than no superheater at all and they are a lot simpler to make and apply. The smokebox temperature of any normal model coal-fired locomotive is certainly considerably higher than the temperature of steam at 80 or 100 lb. per sq. in. pressure (328° F. and 338° F. respectively), more often than not it is likely to exceed 500° F. and in such circumstances there is bound to be some degree of superheating effect, and it is fatuous to refer to such apparatus as " condensers." It is a lamentable fact that after more than 60 years alleged " progress " in model locomotive design and construction we are still completely in the dark regarding most basic facts relating to boiler performance. Nobody has ever published any figures relating to superheat, we just don't have any idea whether we are getting 50° or 250°, nobody knows what vacuum we get in the smokebox, nobody knows what vacuum we get in the firebox, and the list could be added to quite considerably. All these things could be found out fairly easily, without much trouble and with quite simple apparatus.*

Where simplicity is the primary requirement a " gridiron " or " hairpin " superheater in the smokebox is a perfectly reasonable and satisfactory proposition and much simpler to make and instal than the flue tube variety, it is also much more robust and desirable. Where high performance is wanted then the flue tube superheater has it every time.

Considering the proportions of the flue tube superheater, Mr. C. M. Keiller has evolved the following simple formula.

Where area of $A = X$

,, ,, ,, $B = Y$ *Note:* " A " is *inside* dia.

,, cir. ,, $A = M$ " B " is *outside* dia.

,, ,, ,, $B = N$

Then $\dfrac{M - (N \times No.\ of\ elements)}{X - (Y \times No.\ of\ elements)} = 10\ to\ 12$

Thus, suppose $A = \frac{13}{16}$ in.

$B = \frac{9}{32}$ in. (two elements)

we have $\left. \begin{array}{l} M = 2.55 \\ 2N = 1.76 \end{array} \right\} = \left\} \begin{array}{l} \\ \end{array} \right. \dfrac{4.31}{0.394} = 10.9$

$\left. \begin{array}{l} X = 0.518 \\ 2Y = 0.124 \end{array} \right\} = \left\} \right.$

which just about averages out between 10 and 12. This formula seems to work out extremely well in practice and would appear to be quite reliable, and far preferable to use than guesswork.

It should be made clear that in this formula each pass ranks as an element; thus in the diagram shown there are, for formula purposes four elements; actually, of course, we should regard in practice, each unit pair as one element. The trickiest part of the flue tube superheater is the header and these are frequently made with a distinctly clumsy blunt ended external profile. It is much preferable to make them with an outline as streamlined as possible. The point end improves the gas flow, and at the same time offers less temptation for cinders to lodge and build up and block the flue.

Where two complete elements are housed in one flue it is well to step their ends so that one lies well ahead of the other. The headers should be kept well back from the firebox tubeplate not less $3\frac{1}{2}$ to 4 diameters (inside) of the containing flue. The elements should either be brazed into the header with soft brass wire, or preferably I think, with Johnson Matthey's B6, which incidentally, besides having a high melting point 790°-830° C. is comparatively cheap. The use of solid drawn stainless

---

* Written before Mr. J. Ewins presented his paper on a model locomotive boiler test at the S.M.E.E. in 1964.

steel tubes and headers for superheater elements holds out excellent prospects, but this material is relatively expensive, and particular care would be necessary in utilising the correct type of brazing alloy and flux.

The late James Crebbin introduced a form of superheater for model locomotive work which has its good points where the boiler is of the wide-firebox type, well master of its work and does not require to be forced, in other words, one in which the fire does not generate an excessively high temperature. Crebbin's arrangement was quite simple.

It will be seen that two slightly enlarged flues are required for each complete element, one leg bringing the steam from the wet header to the header in the firebox, the other leg taking it back to the hot header in the smokebox. In this form of construction, steel, preferably stainless, must be used for both elements and firebox headers and it is obvious that, for constructional reasons, the joints between elements and firebox headers must be screwed. Where this type of superheater is adopted it is strongly advised that cast iron cylinders, pistons and valves be used, with piston packing in the form of metallic rings. Soft packing is not suitable for high superheat, and gunmetal even less so, excellent though it is for low superheat.*

Turning to the smokebox superheater, two designs are shown in Figs. 8-4 and 8-5; the first a " gridiron," the second a " hairpin." The first is, perhaps, the simplest to make and instal, the second provides the larger superheating area; both provide ample cross-sectional area for the passage of steam, and neither is in the least likely to cause appreciable drop in pressure between boiler and steamchest. Incidentally it is a simple matter temporarily to remove either and connect direct to steamchest, when the effect upon performance can be observed and recorded with a reasonable degree of accuracy.

Turning to superheaters for boilers other than locomotive type, there are a whole galaxy of differing designs, suitable for a wide range of differing types of boiler, and it would obviously be quite impossible to attempt to describe them all; it is proposed, therefore, to deal with only a few of the types most likely to interest the maker of model boilers.

For the simple, externally-fired boiler types shown in Figs. 3-1 to 3-3, a plain loop tube arranged just below the boiler will usually do all that is required; where rather more superheat is required this tube may be bent. In all cases the tube should have easy bends and its bore should be about 50 per cent. bigger than that of the actual steampipe. For a boiler such as that shown in Fig. 3-4 a double header loop tube or " hairpin " is probably the best type, in fact it is a type which, with minor variations in construction and arrangement has a wide variety of application. Such a superheater is detailed in the design for the " K " type boiler.

For vertical boilers some form of coil generally fills the bill most satisfactorily. Such coils may be in the form of single or multiple flat

---

* Since writing the above, a good deal of work has been done, notably by Mr. Ewins on radiant heater superheaters, i.e. superheaters having part of their surface exposed to the fire, *a la* Crebbin, and considerable success has been achieved. Fears of burnt-out elements and lubricating troubles have proved in practice to be without foundation.

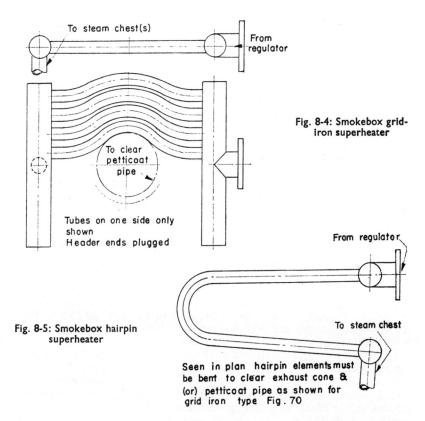

To steam chest(s)

From regulator

Fig. 8-4: Smokebox grid-
iron superheater

To clear
petticoat
pipe

Tubes on one side only
shown
Header ends plugged

From regulator

Fig. 8-5: Smokebox hairpin
superheater

To steam chest

Seen in plan hairpin elements must
be bent to clear exhaust cone &
(or) petticoat pipe as shown for
grid iron type Fig. 70

spirals, or in the form of vertical spirals, single or concentric, like ordinary coil springs. A general principle to be observed wherever possible is that the inlet end of the superheater should be further away from the source of heat than the outlet end, thus following the contra-flow principle of heat transfer. Wherever possible superheaters should be so arranged that the stop valve or regulator is at the *hot* end. There are two sound reasons for this. First by this method the superheater will be kept full of steam when the stop valve is shut, and thus be less liable to damage through burning, and second regulation of the engine is more sensitive, a large superheater contains quite a lot of steam, and if the regulator or stop valve is at the inlet end of the superheater when it is shut this body of steam still has direct access to the engine.

Where the regulating *is* done on the hot end of the superheater, care must be taken that the regulator or valve is of suitable design and material to stand up to the high temperature. Where there is any high degree of superheat, say, over 100° F. over saturated steam temperature, brass, bronze and gunmetal are unsuitable, steel, preferably stainless, Monel metal and cast iron are the metals to use. In a boiler other than a locomotive boiler, it is good practice where possible, to provide an isolating valve on the " wet " side of the superheater. The value of superheating in running model engines can hardly be overstated.

Cylinder condensation is a headache even in the largest reciprocating engines, and the smaller the size the worse it becomes. Superheating is the only practical means for combating this trouble. Where brass or bronze cylinders are used (and particularly does this apply to brass) superheat can only be moderate, it should certainly not exceed 100° F. above saturated steam temperature for the best quality gunmetal and, say, 50° F. for brass. With cast iron cylinders and pistons fitted with C.I. or steel piston rings it can be as high as you are likely to attain with any normal type of model boiler layout.

Don't on any account overlook the fact that where superheated steam is used, it is absolutely essential that lubrication of slide valves (or piston valves) and cylinder shall be adequate and constant, and that a reliable brand of steam superheat oil should be used. Whilst piston valves are undoubtedly better suited to use high superheat steam than are slide valves, within the normal range of the model engineer the latter are unlikely to give any trouble, always provided that lubrication with a suitable quality of oil is adequate. In this connection balanced slide valves are very well worth serious consideration.

Feedwater Heaters. These are a somewhat neglected item in the model engineering world, which is regrettable as they can add substantially to the overall efficiency of any steam plant, even the smallest, whilst they are essentially simple and add no serious complication and no moving parts at all to the plant.

There are two usual methods of feedwater heating, (1) by means of the flue gases, in which case the heater is frequently referred to as an " economiser," which it certainly is, and (2) by utilising part of the exhaust steam. The latter subdivides into (*a*) direct heating, in which the exhaust steam mixes with the feedwater and (*b*) indirect, in which the feedwater and exhaust steam are left separate.

The " economiser " type is largely used in land and marine boilers, and on land the " direct " type exhaust steam heater to a lesser degree. Where feedwater heaters are used on locomotives they are almost always of the indirect type.

For model work both the " economiser " type and the indirect exhaust steam heated types are to be recommended, and they may be used together as they not infrequently are in full size practice, in such a case the feedwater passes through the exhaust feedheater first and thence through the economiser into the boiler. For use on simple externally fired boilers the feedwater heater may be made and applied in exactly the same manner

Fig. 8-6: Contra flow principle feedheater

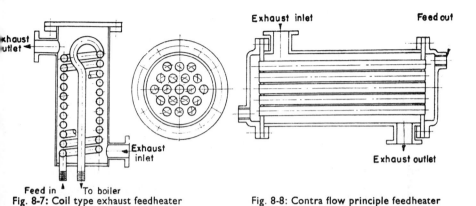

Fig. 8-7: Coil type exhaust feedheater   Fig. 8-8: Contra flow principle feedheater

as the superheater, whilst in boilers of the type shown in Fig. 3-4 Chapter
Three or the Scotch type, a hairpin economiser similar to the hairpin superheater shown in the detail drawings of the K type is to be recommended.
For vertical boilers flat spiral coils or helical coils in the smokebox work
out well. Generally you are unlikely to be able to get too much heating
surface. All feedwater heaters should be so made that they can be fairly
easily dismantled for cleaning. Figs. 8-7 and 8-8 show two types of indirect
exhaust steam heaters, Fig. 8-7 being very much the simplest though not,
perhaps, quite so efficient as Fig. 8-8. It is good practice to put a non-
return valve on the inlet end of the water feed pipe close up to the heater.

Wherever possible the contra-flow principle should be adopted, that is
to say that the feedwater should enter at the end furthest away from the
hot gases or exhaust steam and flow towards them, this greatly improves
the efficiency of heat transfer, the sketch illustrates the principle. (Fig. 8-6.)

Feedwater heating on one or other, or both, of these principles is to
be most thoroughly recommended, it may be expected to cut fuel
consumption by 10 per cent. or better if well carried out; in effect a boiler
supplying steam to an engine and having an efficient feedwater heating
system can be smaller than one without such a system, or alternatively the
addition of a good feedwater heating system will enable a boiler to
steam a bigger engine than it could do without it.

The direct exhaust steam feedwater heating system is not recommended
for model work, as it is impossible with it to prevent the feedwater being
more or less heavily contaminated with lubricating oil carried over from
the cylinder, and it is for practical purposes impossible to separate this
oil afterwards and oil is the very last thing you want in a boiler.

In conclusion, wherever possible install a superheater, a feedwater
heater and lag your boiler as efficiently as possible, by so doing you will
be able very materially to improve its performance.

CHAPTER NINE

Model locomotive-type boilers

THE model locomotive boiler bulks so largely in model engineering that it is considered fully worthy of a chapter to itself. It undoubtedly reaches the acme of performance when used on a model locomotive, but it has worthwhile applications in many other connections; shallow draft steamers, particularly sternwheelers, torpedo boats, portable engines, road locomotives, traction engines and steam rollers, undertype and overtype semi-portable engines, etc.

The high steaming power of a locomotive boiler is largely due to a combination of two things, (1) a relatively high pressure draft, induced by the blast pipe, (2) the vibrations to which the boiler is subjected in running assisting the steam bubbles rapidly to free themselves from the heating surfaces. Used for stationary or marine purposes the locomotive type boiler cannot be forced to anything like the extent possible with the locomotive.

We will deal first with the locomotive type boiler proper. This type of boiler probably involves more work than any other in common use by model engineers, and whatever may be said, it is *not* an easy or simple proposition to make, more particularly for the beginner. Like so many things in engineering it has, for practical reasons, to include in its construction features which are, mechanically speaking, highly undesirable and it is inherently unsuited to working at high pressures. The large flat areas of the firebox have to be supported with a forest of stays, which are expensive to make and instal, and even more expensive to maintain. It is probable that the cost of maintenance and repair of the locomotive boiler, and in particular of its firebox, has been the chief influence in its supersession by the diesel. The locomotive boiler is not only very heavy on repairs but costly in day to day maintenance; it requires frequently washing out if its efficiency is not seriously to suffer, and it is fussy about its feedwater.

None of these drawbacks need worry the model engineer, generally he is not worried about efficiency or economy (to judge by his ready acceptance of almost any old design which will " work," he couldn't care less !).

Three complete designs are included for boilers suitable for model locomotives, one a water-tube firebox type, one a " Smithies " water-tube type and a conventional locomotive type which has been specially designed for the late Henry Greenly's undertype engine of 1903, one of the best stationary engine designs ever to appear in *Model Engineer*, a statement which is supported by the fact that although this is not a scale model of any existing prototype, the Science Museum authorities think sufficiently highly of it to exhibit one at South Kensington as an excellent example of the general type; a pretty high compliment from an exceedingly discriminating and knowledgeable authority.

In offering this modernised version of the boiler, it should be made abundantly clear that no criticism of Greenly or his design is either intended or implied. The original is over 60 years old, and a lot has been learnt in that time; if Greenly were alive today and were designing a boiler to suit this engine, it would almost certainly be modified considerably; I like to think, possibly along the lines of my design.

Reverting to the G.W. type boiler (it might equally well be referred to as " L.M.S." or " B.R.") little need be said about it as the drawings give full particulars. The sizes of tubes, flues and superheater elements have been worked out in accordance with rules formulated by Mr. C. M. Keiller, an article on which was published in the " M.E." June 26th, 1938, and was notable as one of the very few which in the whole history of model locomotive engineering, which has attempted successfully to bring scientific knowledge and disciplined reasoning, to bear on any aspect of model locomotive design. A feature of the superheater is that it provides a much larger total cross sectional area for the passage of steam than is normal; it does not seem to be realised that long superheater elements with sharp return bends (which are practically unavoidable) create considerable friction and unless ample area is allowed there will be a marked drop at high speeds between the pressure in the boiler and the pressure in the steam chest. Long before the full-size locomotive faded out its designers had realised the absolute necessity of being able to maintain, at high power rates of working, a pressure in the steam chest within a very small percentage of that in the boiler. This matter is dealt with more fully in Chapter Eight.

The safety valve is placed in the location usual on the G.W. (but not on the L.M.S. or B.R.) and a baffle plate is fixed beneath it to reduce the tendency to eject water when blowing-off; a valve of non-pop type is best suited to this particular location.

Top feed is separated from the safety valve; to combine the two on a model seems to me to be asking for trouble. The water spaces around the firebox are larger than usually allowed, which has the effect of somewhat reducing the grate area, though not to any appreciable extent, in any case the advantage accruing from increased water space in this vital area are thought far to outweigh any nominal loss of grate area.

This boiler is quite suitable for working at any pressure up to 120 lb. per sq. in. There is considerable scope in the model world for using higher pressures, higher superheats and improved valve and valve gear design and it is along such lines that lies the means of attaining improved performance and greater thermal efficiency.

The second design does not require much comment. Fully detailed drawings of the whole engine and boiler appeared in the " M.E.," Vols. 8 and 9, 1903, together with an excellent coloured plate, sectional elevation, and the boiler detached for replacement fits into the original design.

The chief alterations are as follows. The Belpaire firebox (outer) has been raised to give more steam space and to allow the steam to be collected higher above the normal water level. The " Field " tubes in the firebox have been dispensed with, two arch tubes have been put in the firebox which will improve circulation, and a deflector plate is fitted inside the firehole to prevent cold air flowing directly to the flue tubes every time the firehole door is opened.

In place of the original (14) brass flues $\frac{5}{8}$ in. outside diameter (18) $\frac{7}{16}$ in. copper tubes and (two) $1\frac{1}{8}$ in. superheater flues are substituted, the latter carrying (two) $\frac{9}{32}$ in. outside diameter elements each, which replace the " gridiron " smokebox superheater in the original design.

The boilers fittings and mountings have also been redesigned, an external poppet valve regulator replaces the original " disc-in-tube " internal regulator, two semi-pop safety valves the original single valve, and a double top feed fitting embodying a clack valve for the pump and another for an injector (not fitted on the original) is fitted just behind the smokebox, whilst a unit-body water gauge, with top and bottom shut-down valves and, of course, a blowdown valve is also included.

Castings used in the original for throatplate and both tubeplates are substituted by flanged copper plates. The construction can be brazed or silver soldered throughout, brazed inner firebox and riveted and soft solder caulked outer shell as the builder prefers.

This modified design should give a higher evaporation per B.Th.U. put into it than the original, but that is in no sense a criticism; after all it would be a poor story if in 56 years we had made no progress. Though this is nothing to do with the boiler, it should be pointed out, that in the original engine brass piston rings were specified; with the new boiler these should be replaced by cast iron or steel rings owing to the much higher superheat likely to be attained (the cylinders *are* CI) and the fitting of a reliable mechanical lubricator is strongly recommended.

The next design is for our old friend the Smithies boiler, suitable for a $2\frac{1}{2}$ in. gauge ($\frac{17}{32}$ in. to 1 ft. scale) 4-4-0 or 2-4-0 locomotive of average proportions. There are two variations from the earlier types. First there are fewer water tubes of larger diameter and secondly there is a complete water filled backhead. Neither of these features is original, the water filled backhead was designed by the late H. Greenly for Bassett-Lowke & Co. Ltd. in the form of a casting over 60 years ago.

The method of fitting the tubes to the barrel is attributable to the late Mr. Tom Averill, but is slightly modified. Averill used straight tubes, but these entailed very considerable distortion of the barrel, and with the larger tubes employed in this boiler, it was thought better to put a slight bend in the forward end of the tubes and thus reduce the necessary barrel distortion. Cleaning plugs are inserted in the backhead opposite the tubes.

Fired by an efficient spirit burner this boiler is capable of putting up a good performance, whilst if fired by a silent type of paraffin burner with a totally enclosed firebox all air being taken through the induction tube a much higher performance would be attained. This system was successfully evolved and applied by Mr. J. H. E. Rodgers, see *Model Engineer*, Vol. 119, No. 2992, dated 25 Sept. 1958. Where such a scheme

24. Above: Inside view of firebox: note the lower part of the backhead shows a deepening piece added using a coppersmith's joint. Inside the firebox can be seen a security circulator

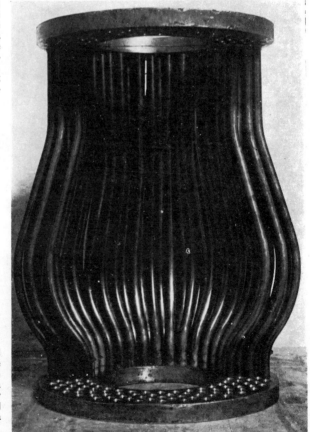

25. Right: A special type of watertube boiler for a steam car (full size, not a model) shown partly tubed. To be fired from the *top* with a sprayburner

26. Above: Inner firebox backplate with firehole ring brazed in place

27. Below: Nicholson thermic syphon fitted to loco inner firebox, made by Martin Evans

is adopted the thickness of the asbestos inner lining of the firebox should be increased as much as possible.

With either form of firing some experiment with blast arrangements would probably be necessary, as neither requires anything like so fierce a draught as does a coal fire. The possibilities of firing with Calor gas have already been referred to, and are a worthwhile field of investigation for the experimentally minded. For either paraffin or Calor gas firing, automatic control of the burner is a perfectly practical proposition and has rewarding possibilities. Such schemes, if they are going to be successfully initiated and carried through, necessitate an open minded approach on the part of the constructor, and a readiness on his part to admit that his preconceived ideas are not necessarily 100 per cent. correct, and to abandon or modify them in the light of experience and as circumstances may dictate.

The last design is a breakaway from the sacred Stephensonian tradition and as such is likely to be unpopular with the troglodytes.

Design No. 14 indicates that in this design, whilst the traditional fire-tube barrel is retained, a water-tube firebox is substituted for the conventional water walled flat sided locomotive type. The construction is very much simpler than that of an orthodox locomotive type boiler and with the exception of the smokebox tubeplate and the throatplate there are no large flat surfaces whatever, whilst stays are largely eliminated. The boiler is obviously admirably suited to high pressure working and the arrangement of the water tube firebox should induce a circulation very much better than that of the normal locomotive type boiler.

This general design lends itself admirably to any size from " O " gauge to 15 in. gauge. The job obviously lends itself to hard soldered construction throughout. The superheater is of the type evolved by the late James Crebbin (" Uncle Jim " to model engineers of goodwill throughout the world), and exposes part of its surface in the firebox itself. For this reason it should be made in stainless steel throughout. The firebox header joints obviously must be screwed to make assembly or dismantling possible, the M.E. standard of 40 t.p.i. is the best thread to use, and it is suggested that the tapped holes in the header should be threaded with a very short taper tap leaving a taper thread, and that the threaded ends of the tubes should be finished taper with a hand chaser, using lots of lubricant and a low speed.

The only awkward job on this boiler is the water-box for the tubes. This could be a casting of high quality gunmetal, but I don't like castings as part of a boiler structure and would prefer to see it built up and sifbronzed or hard-soldered with B.6.

The tubes can then be fixed with silver solder. Such a water box is detailed, and it will be noted that a clearing plug is provided opposite each watertube. In a boiler of this type ebullition in the firebox top header will be pretty violent, so steam should be collected from the main barrel, from a dome of course if possible, otherwise by a perforated pipe. For the same reason the safety valves too should be mounted on the main barrel. It will also be advantageous to use a water gauge mounted on a water column. If a steam fountain is used and mounted in the usual position on top of the boiler inside the cab, then it should be fed by an internal pipe carried well into the barrel, capped and perforated in the usual manner, alternatively if a dome is used, the pipe may collect from this, or if the model is a freelance job the pipe from the dome may be entirely external, in which case it should be well lagged. The firebox sides and " backhead " should have a heavy lagging of fire-tile or " Keislegler " whilst the upper portion should have a lining of thick asbestos millboard. A suggestion which may appeal to the experimentally minded would be to surround the top and sides of the outside of the firebox with a metal jacket, through which the air for combustion would be drawn from the top and supplied at the sides below the firebox, adjustable dampers being fitted to regulate the supply. The sketch (Fig. 9-1) indicates the principle in mind.

If this could be done successfully it would present several advantages, notably keeping the outside of the firebox cool and at the same time supplying pre-heated air to the fire. I have every confidence in recommending a boiler of this type as a worthwhile proposition.

It transgresses no thermal laws, should have an excellent circulation, is straightforward to construct and inherently very strong. I have experimented with such a boiler, spirit and gas fired, on a small scale with most encouraging results. I have, as I said earlier, no doubt that the traditionalists will object to it as a departure from orthodoxy and precedent; I would remind these good people that 135 years ago there was widespread and violent opposition to the steam locomotive itself!

Much more could be written about the locomotive boiler, one of the most useful of all types and certainly one of the most fascinating to build and operate, but considerations of space and for the readers patience forbid.

Suffice it to say that, in model form at any rate, we are by no means at the end of its potentialities. Progress never came from anyone who was satisfied with things as they were, it comes from discontent and a desire to improve things; the ambition may frequently outrun the skill, but without it there will inevitably be stagnation.

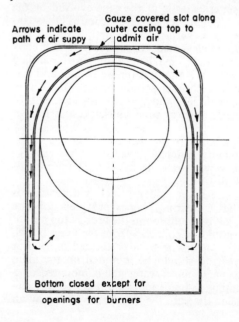

Arrows indicate path of air suppy

Gauze covered slot along outer casing top to admit air

Bottom closed except for openings for burners

(Left)
Fig. 9-1:

BOILER DESIGNS

INTRODUCTORY NOTE

The designs included herewith cover a reasonably wide range of types and sizes of working model boilers, ranging from small power stationary to quite small and simple water tube locomotives.

It could, of course, be extended almost indefinitely, as a casual study of Chapter Three will clearly indicate (and, of course, this only covers a fraction of the *possible* prototypes) but considerations of space set a very definite limit. The types covered all have their useful place in the model engineering world and it is hoped that they will cover the requirements of the majority of readers. Practically all the designs can, by suitable modification, be made in larger or smaller sizes, though it is generally desirable that their proportions should be followed as closely as convenient. It must be borne in mind when varying sizes that the proportions of flue tubes should conform with the rules given in Chapter Eight.

With reference to water-tube boilers, on general principles those having straight tubes are the simplest to construct, though one cannot lay down hard and fast rules. As an example the Bolsover Express type of boiler has spirally coiled tubes, but these being individually much longer than any straight tubes, naturally greatly reduce the number of joints required in construction, incidentally, a most desirable feature.

MODEL BOILER DESIGNS

DESIGN No. 1
HORIZONTAL EXTERNALLY FIRED SMALL POWER BOILER

For anyone requiring a simple small-power boiler this is one that can be thoroughly recommended. The construction is quite straightforward, there is probably nearly as much work in the casing as there is in the actual boiler. The boiler may be made on the riveting and soft solder caulking principle with the tubes fixed by expanding, in which case they should be of a thickness of not less than 18 s.w.g. Alternatively, the whole may be silver soldered; either method properly carried out will be perfectly safe and satisfactory. The type is quite a fast and steady steaming one with a fair range of water level, and it lends itself to the inclusion of a large and efficient superheater. Unless you can fit a chimney of at least 6 ft. to 8 ft. high some form of draught augmentation will be necessary for coal firing, either in the form of a fan or, simpler, a steam blower. Fired with an oil spray burner this could be dispensed with. Of course, if the engine exhaust can be utilised for draught purposes this will suffice and nothing else will be needed when running, though a steam blower will be required when the engine is not running, to provide sufficient draught to keep the fire going. Feed may be supplied by an engine-driven pump, a steam donkey pump or an injector.

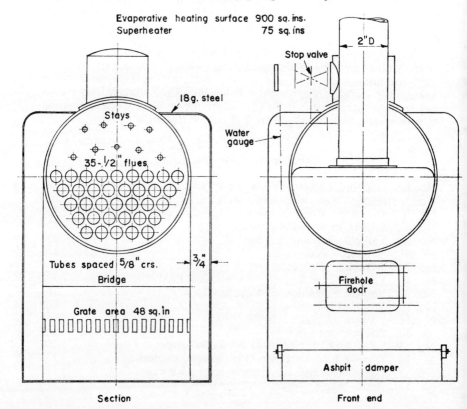

Evaporative heating surface 900 sq. ins.
Superheater 75 sq. ins

Stop valve

2" D

18 g. steel

Stays

35 - ½" flues

Water gauge

Tubes spaced 5/8" crs.

¾"

Bridge

Firehole door

Grate area 48 sq. in

Ashpit damper

Section   Front end

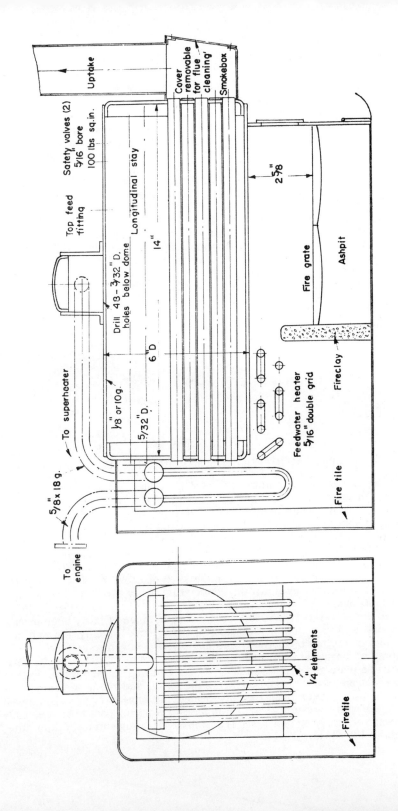

Uptake

Cover removable for flue cleaning'

Smokebox

Safety valves (2)
5/16" bore
100 lbs sq.in.

Top feed fitting

Longitudinal stay

Drill 48 - 3/32" D.
holes below dome

14"

6"D

2⁵⁄8"

Fire grate

Ashpit

To superheater

1/8" or IOg.

5/32" D.

Fireclay

Feedwater heater 5/16" double grid

5/8" x 18 g.

To engine

Fire tile

1/4" elements

Firetile

A hand pump, preferably of the lever type, say, $\frac{5}{8}$ in. bore by 1 in. to 1$\frac{1}{4}$ in. stroke may be provided as a stand-by, but in my view an engine-driven pump and an injector for use when the engine is not running is probably the best proposition; though the steam donkey pump has its attractions it is rather wasteful of steam. From a purely economic point of view the engine-driven pump, always assuming that the pump is well designed and made, is the best bet; that is to say, it will put the least drag on the boiler. It is often stated that the injector is practically 100 per cent. efficient as it puts back into the boiler apart from small radiation losses, all the heat it takes out. This is a misleading view as the heat is put in at a much lower temperature; one has only got to observe what happens to the pressure gauge, with a boiler working near to its capacity when the injector is put into action to realise how unrealistic this claim is. Altogether this is a type of boiler to be thoroughly recommended for small power work.

The evaporative heating surface is about 900 sq. in. or rather over 6 sq. ft. whilst a large superheater and a coil feedwater heater both favourably situated in relation to the hot gases, will add substantially to the overall efficiency of the boiler.

DESIGN No. 2

HORIZONTAL MULTITUBULAR MARINE OR STATIONARY

The horizontal multitubular boiler is a useful and straightforward type for either marine or stationary work and is much more thermally efficient than is the popular centre-flue type, whilst is does not involve very much more work in construction. A spiral coil superheater is located in the smokebox, whilst if desired this (the smokebox) could be extended by a little to accommodate a coil feed heater which would be a distinct help towards fuel economy. This is a type of boiler which should quite definitely be lagged, not only for the sake of economy, but if used for marine work to keep down the temperature inside the hull to reasonable proportions.

A boiler of this type is suitable for a wide range of fairly large marine models and in common with most of the "Tank" family, fits well into a hull of normal proportions and has a very low centre of gravity. If a spray oil burner is used, such as the type shown in Fig. 11, Chapter Five, a baffle plate and inspection door should be fitted to the firebox front to prevent an excess of cold air being drawn in, and the steam supply for it should be taken from the superheater, the pipe carrying it being well lagged with asbestos string. For marine work in particular a reliable means of supplying boiler feed is a "must." Heating surface, evaporative, about 130 sq. in.

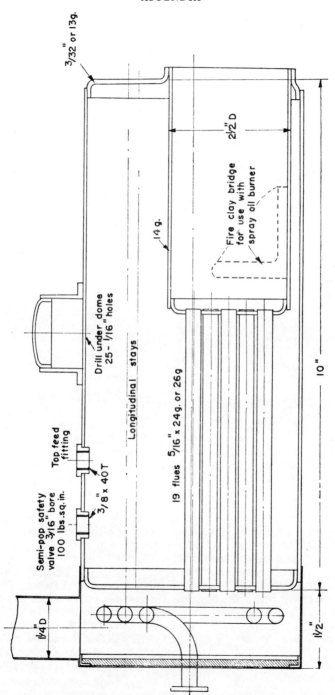

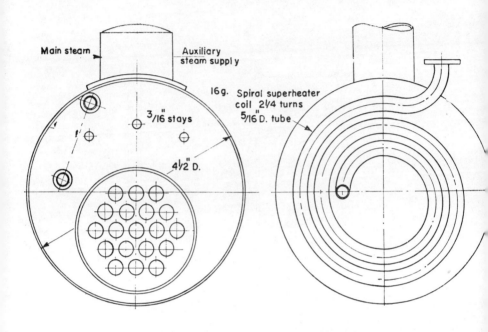

Main steam

Auxiliary
steam supply

16 g. Spiral superheater
coil 2¼ turns
5/16 D. tube

3/16" stays

4½" D.

DESIGN No. 3

HORIZONTAL SELF-CONTAINED CORNISH BOILER

This boiler is one I designed a good few years back as one of a series and was illustrated and described in the *Model Engineer*.   In effect it is a self-contained Cornish boiler with water tubes in the firebox. The boiler proper is our trusty (but rather inefficient, thermally considered) old friend, the centre flue type, but the addition of the outer casing, so arranged that the flue gases after passing through the furnace pass back below the barrel and then forward again along its sides ensures that a far greater proportion of the heat units released by the fuel will be profitably absorbed.   The outer casing also makes possible excellent accommodation for a good-sized superheater and a feedwater heater, the latter being situated in the flue below the boiler barrel.   The portion of the outer shell covered by the dome should not be cut away, but perforated by about 20 holes $\frac{1}{16}$ in. dia.; this saves the necessity for a reinforcing ring below the dome and assists the collection of dry steam. No dimensions are given on the drawing, but as designed the barrel was $3\frac{1}{2}$ in. dia., 8 in. long between ends, whilst the firebox is $1\frac{3}{4}$ in. dia. and the water tubes $\frac{3}{8}$ in. dia. These sizes can, of course, be varied over quite a wide range so long as the approximate general proportions are maintained.   Working pressure 100 lb. per sq. in.; evaporative heating surface about 130 sq. in.

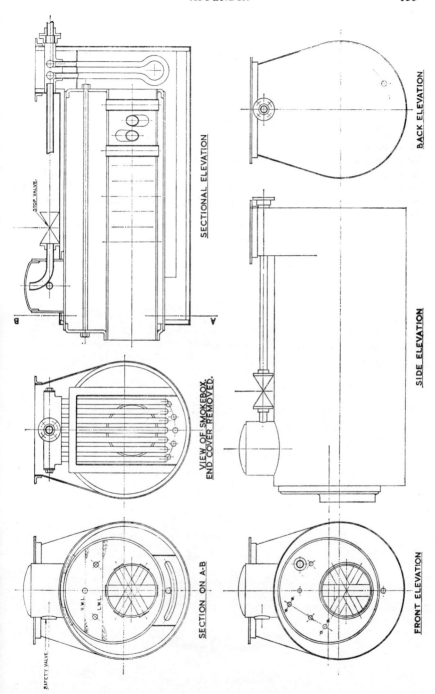

SECTIONAL ELEVATION

STOP VALVE.

BACK ELEVATION

SIDE ELEVATION

VIEW OF SMOKEBOX.
END COVER REMOVED.

SECTION ON A-B

H.W.L.

L.W.L.

SAFETY VALVE

FRONT ELEVATION

DESIGN No. 4

BOILER OF SCOTCH MARINE TYPE, "INGLIS" MODIFICATION

This boiler is suitable for a fairly large model, particularly perhaps for a tug, it disposes a total heating surface (evaporative) of 221 sq. in. plus 28 sq. in. superheater and is suitable to work at anything up to 100 lb. per sq. in. in pressure. It is intended for oil firing, either of the blow-lamp or spray burner type. If the former is used it should give a short, large diameter flame, whilst if a spray burner is used the steam supply should be taken from the superheater and a fireclay wall, shown dotted, inserted in the furnace tube; this will rapidly become bright red hot and serve to reignite the spray should it for any reason, such as a drop of water, become temporarily extinguished.

Steam is taken from the dome via a screw-down stop-valve to the " wet " header of the superheater, whilst a second stop valve should be installed on the delivery line from the " hot " header.

The proportions of this boiler may be varied slightly without detriment, for instance, the length may be increased up to $1\frac{1}{2}$ times the diameter; if the boiler is over $6\frac{1}{2}$ in. long, increase the size of the tubes to $\frac{3}{8}$ in. (this will, of course, necessitate reducing their number and respacing them).

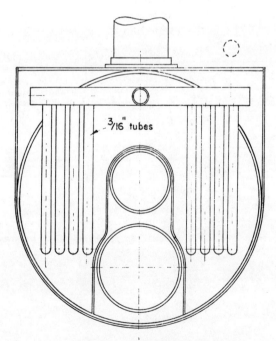

Smokebox end cover removed

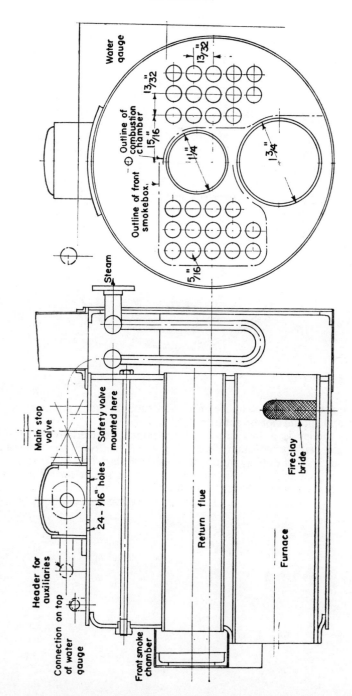

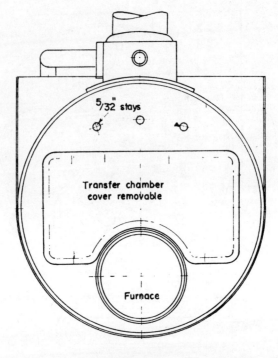

Boiler front

The ratio of furnace and combustion tube to barrel diameter is about right and should not be substantially varied.

This boiler is a fast and steady steamer. Preferably it should be arranged with a constant feed supply, either from an engine-driven pump or a small donkey pump, such as the Stuart Turner. It is distinctly advantageous to include an exhaust steam feedwater heater in the feed line. This is a type of boiler to be thoroughly recommended where weight cutting is of no importance. Evaporative heating surface about 180 sq. in.

DESIGN No. 5

VERTICAL PLAIN MULTITUBULAR

This is a very simple type of boiler, essentially suitable for firing with gas or liquid fuel. It combines compactness with a large heating surface and for this reason should be supplied with a continuous feedwater supply. As with design No. 9 a superheater of the coil type can conveniently be housed in the smokebox. It is a type suitable for working at fairly high pressure, say, up to 150 lb. per sq. in. It can, of course, be built over a very wide size range; as used by the Stanley Steam Car Company it was made up to 30 in. dia. by about 18 in. high with something like 1,200 flue tubes ½ in. dia. ! The small specimen shown has, taking the tubes only and taking only the two-thirds of their length in contact with water about 60 sq. in. of evaporative surface.

Owing to the large heating surface compared with the water content, it is a very rapid steam raiser. An excellent type where simplicity, large heating surface and compactness are required.

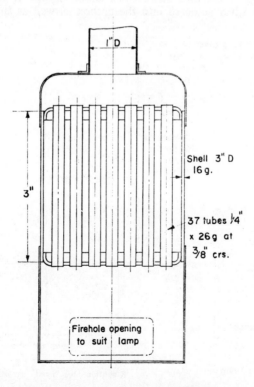

DESIGN No. 6

VERTICAL, SPECIAL TYPE. "HARRIS" ECONOMIC

This is a boiler only likely to appeal to those keen on coppersmithing who require a compact boiler of high evaporative capacity combined with reasonably high thermal efficiency. As shown it is arranged for firing with coal in the normal manner, but it is equally applicable to liquid fuel firing in a regenerative type of burner, either of the bunsen type or white flame type, such as the "Lune Valley." By a slight constructional alteration as indicated on the drawing at *A* it can be top-fired with coal à *la* steam lorry arrangement.

As shown there are no less than 162 tubes, disposing a heating surface of approximately 1.6 sq. ft. (actually 230 sq. in.), but whilst this arrangement will give the best evaporative capacity and the highest thermal efficiency, there is no reason why a smaller number of $\frac{5}{16}$ in. dia. tubes should not be substituted. The tubes should be of light gauge 24 or 26 s.w.g. They should be silver soldered to the shell and expanded into the firebox, though if the alternative construction shown at *A* is adopted, they could be silver soldered into the firebox as well as the shell. The

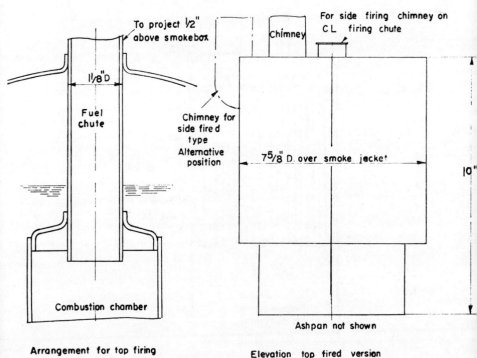

Arrangement for top firing

Elevation top fired version

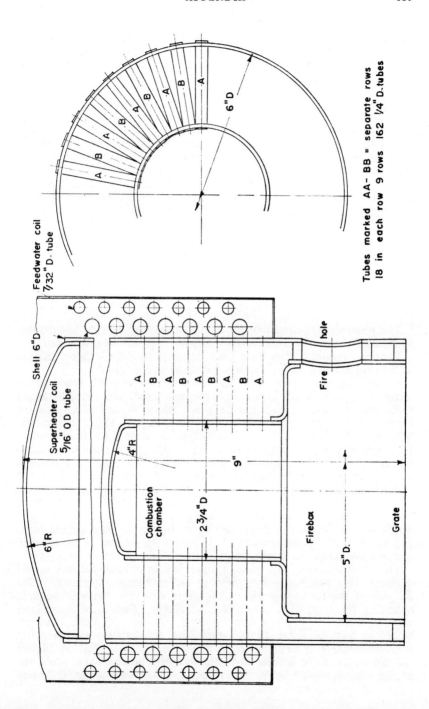

Feedwater coil
7/32" D. tube

Tubes marked AA- BB = separate rows
18 in each row 9 rows 162 1/4" D. tubes

Shell 6"D

Superheater coil
5/16" O D tube

6"D

6"R

Combustion
chamber

4"R

9"

2 3/4" D

Fire
hole

Firebox

5" D.

Grate

tube holes should be drilled with the shell and firebox assembled and held together by a few bolts, if this is done *after* the assembly has been silver soldered together you will have an awful lot of copper drill chips *inside* the boiler which will be very difficult to get out. Drilling should be done by drilling, say, $\frac{1}{8}$ in. dia. pilot holes first and opening out with a cutter as shown as *B*, this will ensure holes of correct size, truly circular. The inclusion of a feedwater heater and superheater, both of large capacity, in the smoke casing will add materially to the evaporative capacity and thermal efficiency of the boiler.

A boiler to appeal to the enthusiast, with excellent steaming characteristics but admittedly one involving a great deal of work. A reliable source of continuous supply of feedwater is essential.

Incidentally, a boiler of this type, increased in size, say, double dimensions, would make an excellent generator for a small steam launch, either (top) coal fired or oil fired with a " Lune Valley " type of burner.

DESIGN No. 7

THE " DUBLIN " ECONOMIC BOILER

The principle of this design for a small coal-fired vertical boiler must be credited to a member of the Dublin S.M.E., hence the cognomen.

Very few model boilers have been designed with the economical use of the heat released by the combustion of the fuel in mind.

As will be seen from an examination of the general arrangement section, the boiler is of the vertical type, coal fired, with firing arranged to be done from the top, a feature which makes it particularly suitable for model steamboat work, where coal firing has been almost completely neglected. The hot products of combustion rise from the firebed through the firebox into the smokebox, from thence they pass downwards through the down-take flues to a secondary smokebox and then through a set of uptake tubes to the chimney, by which time a high proportion of the useful heat will have been given up to the contents of the boiler. A loop superheater is installed in the upper smokebox. The total evaporative surface, neglecting the tubeplates, is about 320 sq. in. made up by firebox 66 sq. in., down-take tubes 142 sq. in. and uptake tubes 112 sq. in., whilst the grate area is about $9\frac{1}{2}$ sq. in. The intended working pressure is 80 lb. per sq. in.

The construction of the boiler should not be difficult for any model engineer who has had some previous boilermaking experience. The flanging of the tubeplates will call for care and skill, but with frequent annealing the work should not be too difficult. Cast G.M. tubeplates *could* be used, but are not recommended. A cast top-plate, however, would be quite in order, though even here, by the time a pattern has been made there is unlikely to be any appreciable saving. A blower for raising steam, or for use when standing will be necessary, whilst the engine exhaust should be conducted to a suitable blast nozzle. If by any

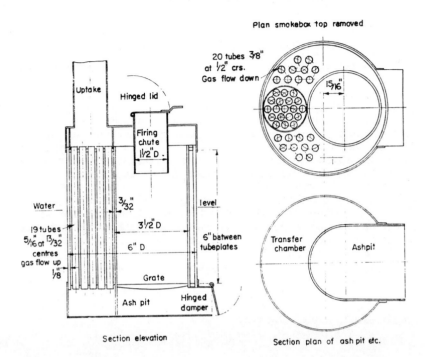

Plan smokebox top removed

20 tubes 3⁄8" at 1⁄2" crs. Gas flow down

Uptake

Hinged lid

Firing chute 1½" D.

Water

level

19 tubes 5⁄16 at 13⁄32 centres gas flow up 1⁄8"

3⁄32"

3½" D

6" D

6" between tubeplates

Grate

Ash pit

Hinged damper

Transfer chamber

Ashpit

15⁄16"

Section elevation

Section plan of ash pit etc.

chance the engine is a condensing one, the blower will probably have to be kept on continuously. Fittings are simple and only those necessary, to wit, direct loaded safety valve, water gauge, protected one-piece body type, pressure gauge, blower valve, feedwater clack, main stop valve and blow-down valve. It is strongly recommended that the boiler shell be thoroughly lagged. This can be done with a lagging steel casing over, say, ¼ in. of flannel soaked in alum, or for those who prefer it with polished strips of mahogany to teak. Either retained in place by bands of brass strip. Evaporative heating surface 320 sq. in.

DESIGN No. 8

VERTICAL SINGLE-FLUE COAL-FIRED

It is probable that more boilers of the vertical single flue type have been built in full size than any other type. They are simple, cheap and easily portable, and they are completely self contained, requiring no brickwork setting, nor elaborate foundations. The type is one which has really not much attraction for the model enthusiast as it is bulky for the amount of heating surface it disposes and it is really only suitable for solid fuel firing. However, it has its good points, it is simple and has comparatively few joints and it carries a fairly large bulk of water related to its heating surface which makes for steady steaming. In full-size work, where steel is used in its construction it suffers badly from corrosion around the uptake flue in the region of the water level, but in model work, where copper is used this is no problem. In larger model boilers of this type where mild steel is used the uptake tube should be considerably thicker than considerations of strength and normal corrosion allowance would dictate.

In the smaller sizes copper as a material for construction and silver soldered joints are the best proposition, in larger sizes mild steel with riveted and caulked joints. The boiler shown in the drawing has around 180 sq. in. evaporative surface. Superheater and/or feedwater heaters are not easy to apply to the type.

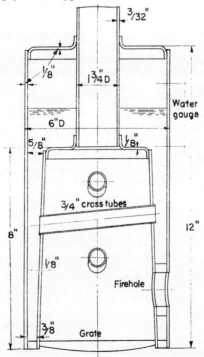

DESIGN No. 9

VERTICAL MULTITUBULAR COAL-FIRED

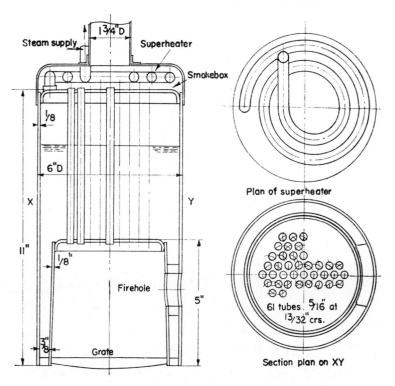

Plan of superheater

Section plan on XY

61 tubes. $\frac{5}{16}$" at $\frac{13}{32}$" crs.

Basically, the vertical multitubular boiler is similar to the vertical centre flue type. From the model engineer's point of view, however, it is altogether superior; it disposes a greatly increased heating surface and makes much better use of the heat released from the combustion of the fuel, whilst the smokebox can be arranged to house a superheater and a feedwater heater, which add greatly to the overall thermal efficiency. Like the centre flue type, it is only really suited to solid fuel firing. If gas or oil firing is preferred, then the simpler plain vertical multitubular Design No. 5 is the better proposition. In the smaller sizes copper and silver soldering construction, in the larger sizes mild steel, riveting and caulking, with brass or copper solid drawn flues expanded at each end. The boiler shown has an evaporative heating surface (submerged portion of flue tubes only taken) of 300 sq. in. which is about 66 per cent. greater than that of the single flue type of exactly similar overall size. All these vertical " tank " boilers should be thoroughly lagged and they lend themselves to this being done quite easily.

Design No. 10

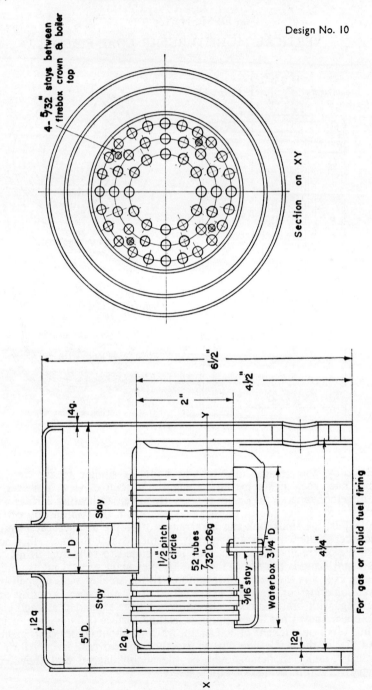

Section on XY

4- 5/32" stays between firebox crown & boiler top

6 1/2"

4 1/2"

2"

14g.

Stay

1" D.

Stay

5" D.

12g

12g

1 1/2" pitch circle

52 tubes 7/32" D. 26g

3/16 stay

Waterbox 3/4" D

4 1/4"

12g

X

Y

For gas or liquid fuel firing

DESIGN No. 10

HAYSTACK OR NAPIER BOILER

This design for a simplified version of the marine " Haystack " boiler (the design of which was, I believe, attributable to Napier) will produce a fast and steady steaming boiler. The type was largely used for paddle steamers and was almost always built with a hemispherical top, which usually came above the main deck.

The hemispherical top is not an easy constructional proposition for the amateur coppersmith and with this in mind a flat has top been substituted. In the full-size job, too, the water box was a really complicated piece of work and this also has been greatly simplified; it would probably improve the circulation if a series, say, four or six, water tubes were added between bottom of firebox and waterbox.

Where such a boiler is adopted for stationary work the height overall, relative to the diameter, could well be increased up to 50 per cent., and, of course, solid fuel firing could be adopted, too.

In the full-sized boilers of this type it was usual to provide four fireholes symetrically spaced around the firebox.

Construction is quite straightforward, copper being the preferable material with silver soldered joints throughout. The boiler disposes around 130 sq. in. evaporative heating surface. A drawback to the type is the difficulty of applying a superheater or feedwater heater.

DESIGN No. 11

YARROW BOILER

The Yarrow boiler is, for the model engineer, one of the best of the watertube family. It is a very fast steamer and will stand considerable forcing; square inch for square inch it has perhaps the highest evaporative capacity of any, with the possible exceptions of the " Lune Valley " Bolsover Express or Monotube types. Its construction is quite straightforward using copper and silver solder whilst its casing arrangement

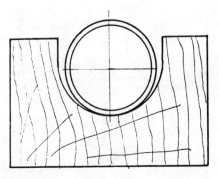

Forming the water headers by the use of a wooden trough

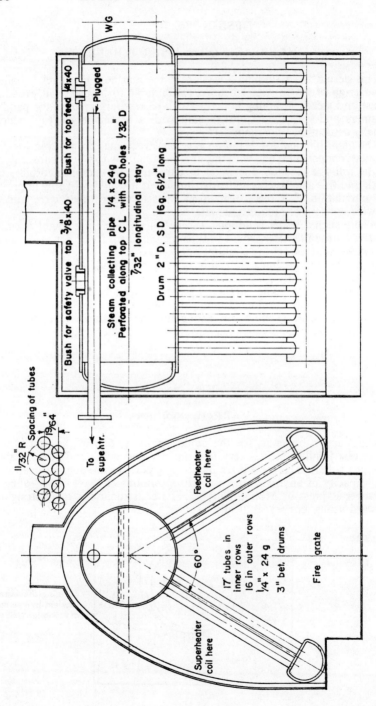

WG

Bush for top feed 1/4x40

Plugged

Bush for safety valve tap 3/8"x40

Steam collecting pipe 1/4 x 24g
Perforated along top C L with 50 holes 1/32 D
7/32" longitudinal stay

Drum 2"D. SD 16g. 6½" long

Spacing of tubes

11/32" R

19/64"

To supehtr.

Feedheater coil here

60°

17 tubes in inner rows
16 in outer rows
1/4" x 24 g
3" bet. drums

Fire grate

Superheater coil here

provides excellent accommodation for a large superheater and feedwater heater. It is equally applicable to gas, liquid fuel or solid fuel firing and it is also well adapted to working at high (from the model engineer's standpoint) pressures; up to 150 lb. per sq. in. or even higher. The only job in its construction which may give some trouble is the forming of the water headers. The best way that I have found for doing this is to make a wooden trough as shown in the sketch, with a radius rather larger than that of the tube, and using a flat faced mallet (not a hammer) gently to flatten out the upstanding portion of the tube, which should be thoroughly annealed first. It would certainly pay the inexperienced to experiment first with one or two short ends of tube.

The boiler shown in the drawing is quite small, but as long as the general proportions are followed sizes may be safely varied. For constructional reasons it is *not advised* that more than two rows of tubes be used. A reliable means of supply a constant supply of feedwater is an absolute necessity, as the water content, relative to the evaporative capacity is very small.

DESIGN No. 12

SCOTT MARINE OR STATIONARY BOILER

The Scott boiler has not, so far as I know, any full-sized prototype; it was named after its inventor, Mr. David Scott, whose name will be familiar to those possessing volumes of the " M.E." from about 1900 to 1910, as a speed boat enthusiast of the days before the Hydroplane and long before either the flash steam plant or the I.C. engine. It is a fast steamer but, like the Yarrow, it requires a constant and reliable feedwater system. The construction is quite simple and the boiler is suitable for a range of working pressures similar to those applicable to the Yarrow. There is ample accommodation in the casing for an efficient superheater and feedwater heater. Firing by gas or liquid fuel is the obvious method, and with the latter the " silent " type of burner is certainly the best. A simple and thoroughly reliable type for small and medium sized models. The example shown disposes about 100 sq. in. of evaporative surface.

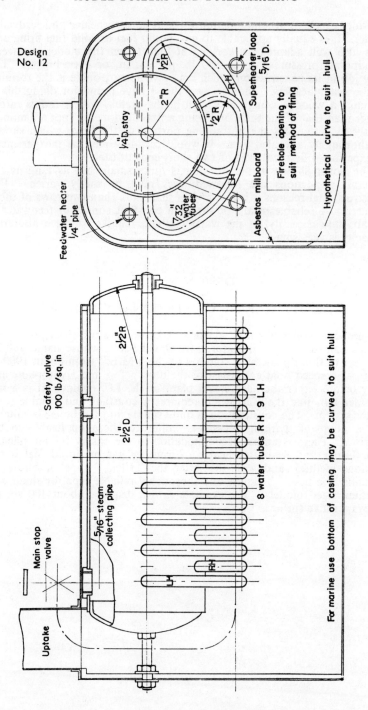

Design No. 12

DESIGN No. 13

" SMITHIES " BOILER FOR 1¾ in. GAUGE LOCOMOTIVE

The " Smithies " model locomotive boiler was invented by the late Fred Smithies around the turn of the century, and it was a major contribution to the craft of model locomotive building. It has been widely used ever since, both by amateurs and the model trade, though its inventor made precious little out of it.

Those whose memories go back to the early twenties will remember the " battle of the boilers " which raged with much sound and fury in the colums of the " M.E." over a long period. This argument always struck me as being largely unrealistic, for it was rather like comparing a wrist watch with a grandfather clock; both serve the same general purpose, but their characteristics are utterly different. So with the " Smithies " and the true locomotive-type model boiler.

Nobody having any knowledge of the facts contests that bulk for bulk the locomotive type will produce more steam or that it is the more realistic; on the other hand, nobody can dispute that the former, the locomotive type, is very much more complicated and expensive than is the " Smithies " type and nothing like so simple a proposition for the beginner to tackle. The fact remains that both have their definite sphere of usefulness in the scheme of things and where simplicity and cheapness are primary considerations, the " Smithies " type has everything in its favour. Much has been made of the " enormous " heat losses suffered by the " Smithies " type through the outer casing, but actually the locomotive type is really worse in this respect, especially if, as is so often the case with small models, the boiler is unlagged. If the outer case of the " Smithies " type is well lined with asbestos millboard (or in larger sizes made double) the heat losses are not serious, whilst the steam producing portion is completely surrounded by hot gases and is not subject to any appreciable radiation losses. The unlagged locomotive-type boiler, on the other hand, puts the heat into the water and steam on the inside and then radiates a not inconsiderable portion of it through the barrel. If a proper test were carried out between two boilers, one of each type, first indoors and then outdoors in unfavourable weather conditions, the falling-off in performance of the locomotive type under the latter conditions, would almost certainly be much greater than that of the " Smithies " type.

Methylated spirit has, weight for weight, a much lower calorific value than has good steam coal, something like 40 per cent. less in fact, and bearing this in mind, one does not have to be a senior wrangler to deduce that to produce a given evaporation you will have to burn a greater weight of spirit than of coal ! This applies quite irrespective of the type of boiler in which it is burnt. Spirit firing has, over a long period, been much maligned, but it has a definite place in the model steam engine world, and this applies with particular force to indoor operation, or where simplicity and convenience are important.

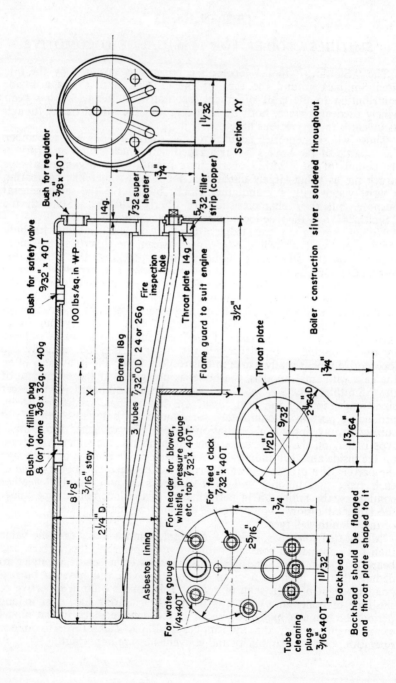

Section XY

Bush for regulator
3/8" x 40T

Bush for safety valve
9/32" x 40T

Bush for filling plug
8 (or) dome 3/8 x 32g. or 40g

100 lbs/sq. in WP.

14g.

7/32 super heater

5/32 filler strip (copper)

Throat plate 14g

Fire inspection hole

Flame guard to suit engine

Barrel 18g

3 tubes 7/32" OD 24 or 26g

8 1/8"

3/16" stay

2 1/4" D

X

Asbestos lining

For header for blower, whistle, pressure gauge etc. tap 7/32"x 40T.

For feed clack 7/32" x 40T

For water gauge 1/4x40T

Tube cleaning plugs 3/16"x40T

Backhead

3 1/2"

1 11/32"

2 5/16"

1 3/4"

Throat plate

Throat plate

1/2" D

9/32"

2 1/64 D

1 13/64"

1 3/4"

1 3/4"

1 11/32"

Boiler construction silver soldered throughout

Backhead should be flanged and throat plate shaped to it

The boiler shown is quite a small one, suitable for a 1¾ in. gauge 4-4-0 locomotive with outside cylinders. Its longitudinal dimensions, both as to barrel and firebox may be varied within reasonable limits to adapt it to the 4-4-2 or 4-6-0 wheel notation, and, of course, as it stands it would suit a 4-4-2, though the driving wheel diameter would probably have to be kept down to a scale 5 ft. 8 in.

The water tubes are rather larger than are usually specified for this size of boiler and should be of light gauge, they are fixed in the barrel by the Averill method, i.e. by drilling plain holes in the shell and then distorting them with a piece of $\frac{7}{32}$ in. dia. silver steel, so that the tubes can enter at the correct angle.

The combined backhead and downcomer adds a little to the constructional work involved, but is, in my opinion, well worth the extra trouble. It improves circulation to some extent and it has the advantage of providing ample space for fittings. Both superheater and feedwater heater are included. If blued lagging steel is used for the outer casing, it can be left in its natural state in a freelance model, which obviates any possibility of paint burning and has a very pleasant appearance. A good many years ago some very fine Baltic (4-6-4) tank engines were built for the G. & S.W.R. which had their boiler lagging finished thus, and they were very good-looking engines.

The " Smithies " boiler is simple and quite reasonably efficient, in fact, for *spirit firing*, probably more efficient than the locomotive type. It should, of course, be silver-soldered throughout. Such boilers have been applied successfully to model locomotives up to as large as 1½ in. scale, though in the larger sizes, fired by paraffin, burnt in the silent regenerative type of burner.

Probably the best system here is to use a burner which takes *all* its air through the induction tube, the burner pan making an airtight joint with the firebox foundation ring. In this case it is usually necessary to work the burner at a pressure which may be anything between 60 and 120 lb. per sq. in. This was the system universally adopted by such cars as the Turner-Miesse, White, and Stanley of which I had much experience and it gave most efficient results.

DESIGN No. 14

BOILER FOR 2½ in. GAUGE LOCOMOTIVE

This boiler was designed specifically for a 2½ in. gauge 0-4-4 tank engine (actually a modernised version of the late Henry Greenly's *Model Engineer* locomotive of 1904) to be fired by methylated spirit, but by modifications of the barrel, it could equally well be applied to an " Atlantic " or " Pacific " type. As will be apparent from an examination of the drawings, it combines a normal firetube barrel with a watertube firebox. This idea was developed with a view to the fuel, methylated spirit, to be used. Methylated spirit has a much lower calorific value than has steam coal, and it burns with a lower temperature, consequently the part of the boiler which comes into direct contact with the flames is, from an evaporative point of view, the most efficient, if at the same time as providing a reasonable area of such heating surface, it is also arranged to give a vigorous circulation, the evaporative efficiency will thereby be increased.

The arrangement of this firebox is such as to provide ample heating surface so disposed as to promote rapid circulation, and thus to produce ample evaporation. Very broadly one may regard the firebox as the steam generator and the barrel as the economiser, though of course, the latter will contribute appreciably to direct evaporation as well. The firebox contributes 51 sq. in. of heating surface, the flues and tubes 67 sq. in. and the superheater, which is partly exposed directly to the flames, 22 sq. in., a total of 140 sq. in. obtained without any crowding of the water tubes or flues.

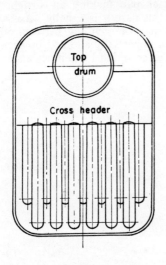

Section 'AB'

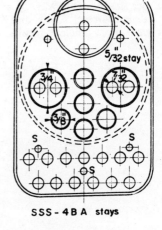

SSS - 4 B A stays

Section 'XY'

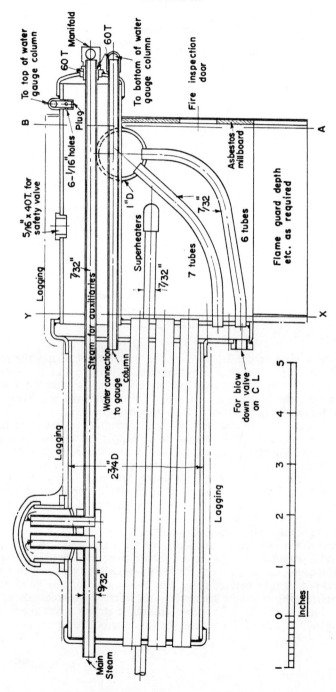

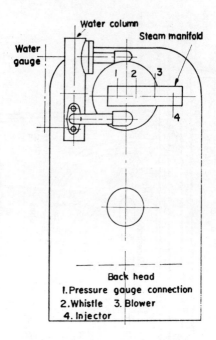

Back head
1. Pressure gauge connection
2. Whistle   3. Blower
4. Injector

This boiler is a very much simpler one to construct than is the normal locomotive type; it requires a minimum of staying whilst the waterbox is the only feature which calls for anything but the simplest flanging. As arranged, the boiler is intended to be used with the regulator of the slide valve pattern, incorporated in the cylinder unit, a revival of a practice much used in the early days of locomotives, and one having distinct advantages, but it would be a simple matter to modify the arrangement to incorporate a regulator in the dome. It may be noted that the main steam pipe and superheaters provide a clear steam passage to the cylinders rather more than twice the area frequently allowed, there is not much point in working at 80 or 100 lb. per sq. in. if when the locomotive is running fast you can only maintain a fraction of this pressure in the steam chest. This boiler is intended to be silver-soldered throughout using, say, Johnson Matthey's B.6 for the waterbox, top and cross drum, etc., and " Easiflo " for the water tubes, flues and fire tubes and front tubeplate. As there is certain to be considerable turbulence in the top drum, the connections for the water column for the water gauge are arranged to take care of this. For those who for any good reason prefer spirit firing and there are many cases where it has great advantages, such a boiler as this is to be recommended, it strikes a balance between the simpler " Smithies " boiler and the full locomotive-type.

DESIGN No. 15

LOCO-TYPE BOILER FOR UNDERTYPE SEMI-PORTABLE

In the first issue of the *Model Engineer* for 1903 there appeared a coloured plate of the G.A. of a compound undertype engine designed by the late Henry Greenly, and fully detailed drawings and instructions

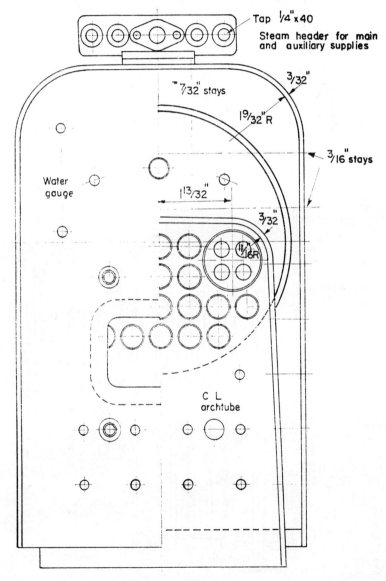

Design No. 15

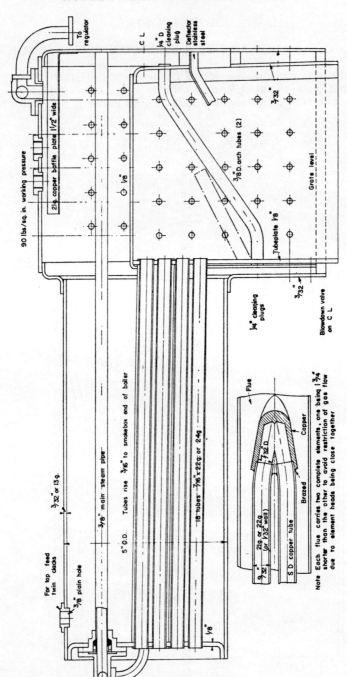

To regulator

C L

¼" D cleaning plug

Deflector stainless steel

³⁄₃₂"

³⁄₈" D. arch tubes (2)

⅛"

90 lbs/sq. in. working pressure

21g. copper baffle plate 1½" wide

Grate level

Tubeplate ⅛"

¼" cleaning plugs

³⁄₃₂"

Blowdown valve on C L

³⁄₃₂" or 13g.

For top feed twin clacks

³⁄₈" plain hole

5" O.D.

³⁄₈" main steam pipe   Tubes rise ³⁄₁₆" to smokebox end of boiler

18 tubes ⁷⁄₁₆" × 22g. or 24g.

⅛"

⅛"

Flue

⁷⁄₃₂" D.

Copper

21g. or 22g. (or ¹⁄₃₂" wall)

Brazed

³⁄₃₂"

⁹⁄₃₂"

S D copper tube

Note Each flue carries two complete elements, one being 1¾" shorter than the other to avoid restriction of gas flow due to element heads being close together

followed in succeeding issues. This was one of the finest complete designs for a stationary steam engine that has ever been published in the *Model Engineer*.

This statement is borne out by the fact that there is in the Science Museum at South Kensington a very fine model built to this design. The Science Museum authorities are rightly very particular about the authenticity of the models they display. In the case of the Greenly model, this conforms to no prototype, but is exhibited as—" an excellent example of the general class "; an outstanding tribute to a very great model engineer.

In putting forward an alternative design of boiler for this engine, it should be made absolutely clear that there is no criticism of the original or of its designer either implied or intended. The design is 60 years old and in that period much has developed; Greenly himself, were he still alive, would be one of the first to take advantage of the greater knowledge we now possess and the improved constructional techniques available to us.

Dimensionally externally the revised boiler conforms to the original except inasmuch as the Belpaire firebox (outer) top is raised to provide greater steam space. Greenly used castings for some of the boiler plates, these have been replaced by flanged copper plates. He also used Field tubes in the firebox, these have been eliminated and a pair of arch tubes and a deflector plate inside the firehole added. The chief alteration lies in the application of a four element flue-tube superheater, located in two large flues and the re-arrangement of the tubes. The original internal " disc-in-tube " regulator is replaced by an external poppet valve regulator. The total evaporative heating surface is, by pure chance, unaltered at 480 sq. in. but to this must be added 64 sq. in. of superheater surface.

The result of these various modifications should be to produce a boiler which will have a higher efficiency than the original and one which will have a markedly higher evaporative capacity. Were Greenly still alive I like to think that he would approve.

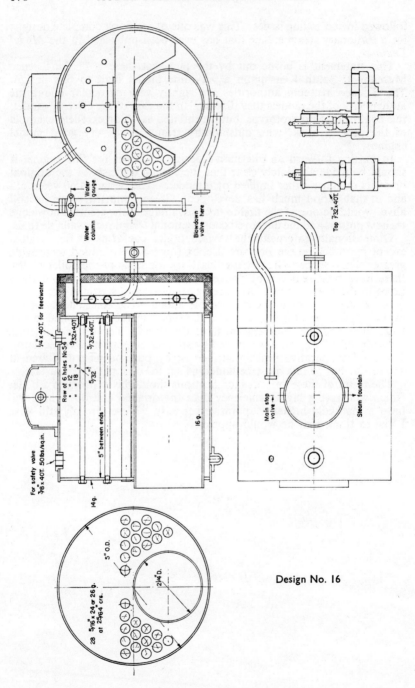

Design No. 16

APPENDIX 179

DESIGN No. 16

SCOTCH MARINE TYPE

The Scotch boiler illustrated was originally designed to supply steam to the small pair of D.A. paddle oscillating engines described in " Model Stationary and Marine Steam Engines " Second Edition.

For its size and power it may, by some, be regarded as unnecessarily elaborate, but the idea was that the complete power unit should follow, as closely as reasonably practical, the principles and appearance of a full-size plant. Actually the boiler would be capable of supplying steam to a larger unit than the engine in question.

The boiler is of the " dry-back " type, an arrangement which provides excellent accommodation for a coil superheater (the engine itself includes an exhaust steam feedwater heater) and excellent facility for tube cleaning.

The outer shell should be made from a piece of 5 in. O/S dia. solid drawn copper tube $5\frac{1}{2}$ in. long whilst the furnace tube is of similar material $2\frac{1}{4}$ in. dia. O/S, and $5\frac{3}{4}$ in. long. The flue tubes are $\frac{5}{16}$ in. dia., $5\frac{1}{2}$ in. long and 24 or 26 s.w.g., again SD copper. The construction is entirely by silver soldering. No flanging is required to the end-plates and if carefully fitted to both outer tube and furnace tube and thoroughly silver soldered they will be perfectly safe, as the boiler is primarily designed for a comparatively low working furnace to suit an oscillating engine. As will be seen, a water column is provided upon which to mount the water gauge; in a boiler of this type and size this is about the only satisfactory way a reliable and easily visible gauge can be mounted. A blowdown valve can be accommodated at the junction of the vertical and horizontal limbs of the water connection. For the sake of cleanliness, the blowdown valve should have a waste-pipe fitted to it and led outboard of the hull. The safety valve shown may be thought unnecessarily elaborate, the reason has already been explained. A simple direct loaded valve would be perfectly satisfactory, though there is a good deal to be said for arranging to enclose it and fit a waste pipe to carry the steam out of the engine room and up a pipe abaft the funnel. Of course, anyone who objects to the unflanged end-plates can flange them, it means rather more metal and considerably more work, and for all practical purposes, the boiler will be no better, it is obviously purely a matter of personal choice for the builder.

Neglecting the back tubeplate, there is about 160 sq. in. of heating surface.

For maximum output a Stuart blowlamp burner would suit well, for lesser output a vaporising spirit burner would be quite satisfactory.

It is not recommended that this type of boiler should be made less than 4 in. O/S dia. with a $1\frac{1}{4}$ in. O/S dia. furnace, in the upward direction there is no limit, I believe in full-size such boilers have in the past been made up to 17 ft. dia. with shell-plates of 2 in. or more thickness. In general this is an excellent type of boiler, a good steam producer and one which has a good thermal efficiency. Its history in full-size Marine work

has been a long and honourable one, until the advent of the Watertube
boiler (and for some considerable time after) it was the mainstay of the
Mercantile Marine as well as of the Royal Navy.

TABLE 1. PROPERTIES OF SATURATED STEAM

Pressure above atmosphere lb. sq. in.	Temperature degrees F.	Total heat B.Th.U.	Volume cu. in. steam from 1 cu. in. water
10	240	1,154	1,036
15	250	1,158	838
20	259	1,160	726
25	267	1,163	640
30	274	1,165	572
35	281	1,167	518
40	287	1,169	474
45	292	1,171	437
50	298	1,172	405
55	303	1,174	378
60	307	1,175	354
65	312	1,176	333
70	316	1,178	318
75	320	1,179	298
80	324	1,180	283
85	328	1,181	270
90	331	1,182	257
95	334	1,183	247
100	338	1,184	237
110	344	1,186	219
120	350	1,188	203
130	356	1,190	190
140	361	1,191	179
150	366	1,193	169
160	371	1,194	159
170	376	1,196	152
180	378	1,197	145
190	384	1,199	138
200	388	1,200	132

TABLE 2. CALORIFIC VALUE OF FUELS

Fuel	Calorific value per lb. B.Th.U.	Calorific value per cu. ft. B.Th.U.
Hydrogen	52,290	293
Acetylene	21,850	1,624
Coal Gas	21,400	685
Calor Gas	{ 21,660 Propane { 21,300 Butane	2,560 3,200
Petrol	19,500	
Paraffin	19,000	
Methylated Spirit	11,000	
Hard Wood	7,400 average	
Charcoal	12,000	
Steam Coal	13,000-15,000	
Coke	12,400	

NOTE.—Different authorities give slightly varying figures, but the above can be taken as a fair average, certainly quite sufficiently accurate for all model engineering purposes.

182   MODEL BOILERS AND BOILERMAKING

TABLE 3. TUBE CIRCUMFERENCES, AREAS, Etc., BASED ON OUTSIDE DIAMETERS

Tube dia. o/s	Circumference inches	Area per 1 foot run sq. in.	Length per 1 sq. ft. area ft.	Length per 100 sq. in. area ft.	Cross section area sq. in.
$\frac{1}{8}$	0·392	4.7	30·5	21·2	0·0122
$\frac{5}{32}$	0·490	5·87	24·5	17·0	0·0192
$\frac{3}{16}$	0·589	7·05	20·4	14·3	0·0276
$\frac{7}{32}$	0·687	8·25	17·5	12·15	0·0376
$\frac{1}{4}$	0·785	9·40	15·3	10·60	0·049
$\frac{9}{32}$	0·883	10·60	13·6	9·45	0·062
$\frac{5}{16}$	0·981	11·80	12·2	8·50	0·077
$\frac{3}{8}$	1·178	14·10	10·2	7·10	0·110
$\frac{7}{16}$	1·374	16·50	8·75	6·07	0·150
$\frac{1}{2}$	1·570	18·85	7·65	5·31	0·196
$\frac{9}{16}$	1·76	21·1	6·80	4·72	0·248
$\frac{5}{8}$	1·96	23·5	6·10	4·24	0·306
$\frac{3}{4}$	2·35	28·1	5·12	3·57	0·441
$\frac{7}{8}$	2·74	33·0	4·36	3·03	0·601
1	3·14	37·7	3·82	2·65	0·785
$1\frac{1}{8}$	3.53	42·2	3·40	2·36	0·994
$1\frac{1}{4}$	3·92	47·0	3·06	2·12	1·227
$1\frac{3}{8}$	4·31	51·7	2·79	1·94	1·485
$1\frac{1}{2}$	4·71	56·5	2·55	1·77	1·767

TABLE 4. GAUGES AND WEIGHTS OF SHEET COPPER PER SQ. FOOT

S.W.G.	Thickness inches	Wt. per sq. ft. lb.	S.W.G.	Thickness inches	Wt. per sq. ft. lb.
0	0·324	14·7	14	0·080	3·65
1	0·300	13·6	15	0·072	3·26
2	0·276	12·5	16	0·064	2·90
3	0·252	11·5+	$\frac{1}{16}''$	0·0625	2·89
$\frac{1}{4}''$	0·250	11·5	17	0·056	2·59
4	0·232	10·5	18	0·048	2·22
5	0·212	9·6	19	0·040	1·83
6	0·192	8·75	20	0·036	1·63
$\frac{3}{16}''$	0·1875	8·66	$\frac{1}{32}''$	0·0312	1·44
7	0·176	7·95			
8	0·160	7·30			
$\frac{5}{32}''$	0·156	7·20			
9	0·144	6·54			
10	0·128	5·82			
$\frac{1}{8}''$	0·125	5·77			
11	0·116	5·28			
12	0·104	4·65			
13	0·092	4·12			

TABLE 5. RECOMMENDED SCREW THREADS FOR FITTINGS PIPES, Etc.

For steam fittings		For pipes	
Dia. of fitting	Thread	Pipe dia.	Thread
$\frac{1}{8}''$	M.E. 40 t.p.i.	$\frac{3}{32}''$	40 t.p.i.
$\frac{5}{32}''$	,, ,, ,,	$\frac{1}{8}''$	40 ,,
$\frac{3}{16}''$	,, ,, ,,	$\frac{5}{32}''$	40 ,,
$\frac{7}{32}''$	,, ,, ,,	$\frac{3}{16}''$	40 ,,
$\frac{1}{4}''$	,, ,, ,,	$\frac{7}{32}''$	40 ,,
$\frac{9}{32}''$	,, ,, ,,	$\frac{1}{4}''$	40 ,,
$\frac{5}{16}''$	,, 32 ,,	$\frac{9}{32}''$	40 ,,
$\frac{3}{8}''$	,, ,, ,,	$\frac{5}{16}''$	40 ,,
$\frac{7}{16}''$	,, ,, ,,	$\frac{3}{8}''$	40 ,,
$\frac{1}{2}''$	,, ,, ,,	$\frac{7}{16}''$	40 ,,
Above $\frac{1}{2}''$	Standard brass, thread 26 t.p.i.	$\frac{1}{2}''$	40 ,,
		$\frac{5}{8}''$	26 ,,
		$\frac{3}{4}''$	26 ,,

TABLE 6. STRENGTH OF ROUND COPPER STAYS

Thread size	Area at bottom of thread sq. in.	Safe *working* load in lbs.
7 B.A.	0·0043	10·4
6 B.A.	0·0055	13·7
5 B.A.	0·0073	18·1
$\frac{1}{8}''$ Whit.	0·0069	17·2
4 B.A.	0·0093	23·2
$\frac{5}{32}'' \times 40$	0·0122 ⎫	30·5
3 B.A.	0·0122 ⎭	
2 B.A.	0·0164	41
$\frac{3}{16}'' \times 40$	0·0191	47·5
1 B.A.	0.0210	52·5
0 B.A.	0·0271	67
$\frac{1}{4}'' \times 40$	0·0375	94
$\frac{5}{16}'' \times 32$	0·058	145
$\frac{3}{8}'' \times 32$	0·088	220

NOTE.—Phosphor-bronze stays (drawn quality) may be taken as 25 per cent. stronger than copper, Monel metal as twice the strength of copper.

TABLE 7. SAFETY VALVE SIZES. SINGLE VALVE. BASED ON A CLEAR UNOBSTRUCTED OPENING EQUAL TO THE BORE

Boiler heating surface sq. in.	Working pressure					
	25	50	75	100	125	150
50	$\frac{3}{16}$"	$\frac{9}{64}$"	$\frac{7}{64}$"			
100	$\frac{1}{4}$"	$\frac{3}{16}$"	$\frac{5}{32}$"	$\frac{1}{8}$"		
200	$\frac{3}{8}$"	$\frac{1}{4}$"	$\frac{7}{32}$"	$\frac{3}{16}$"	$\frac{11}{64}$"	$\frac{5}{32}$"
300	$\frac{7}{16}$"	$\frac{5}{16}$"	$\frac{1}{4}$"	$\frac{7}{32}$"	$\frac{13}{64}$"	$\frac{3}{16}$"
500	$\frac{9}{16}$"	$\frac{13}{32}$"	$\frac{21}{64}$"	$\frac{9}{32}$"	$\frac{17}{64}$"	$\frac{15}{64}$"
700	$\frac{5}{8}$"	$\frac{15}{32}$"	$\frac{27}{64}$"	$\frac{21}{64}$"	$\frac{5}{16}$"	$\frac{19}{64}$"
1,000	$\frac{13}{16}$"	$\frac{9}{16}$"	$\frac{15}{32}$"	$\frac{15}{32}$"	$\frac{25}{64}$"	$\frac{3}{8}$"

NOTE:—For 300 sq. in. H.S. and over, two valves are recommended, one set for working pressure and one 5 lb. sq. in. higher. Where two valves are used their bores may be 0.71 of that of a single valve. The sizes given relate to medium steaming boilers, for boilers of high steaming capacity, intensively fired, use next size larger.

TABLE 8. PROPERTIES OF J.M. Co. SILVER BRAZING ALLOYS

Brazing alloy	Melting range °C.	Tensile strength tons sq. in.	Relative cost 1 = highest	Data sheets giving additional information
Type 5	698-788	26	6	
" Easy-flo "	620-630	30	4	Data Sheet 2121
Easy-flo No. 2 ..	608-617	30	5	,, ,, 2122
Argo-flo	605-651	32	7	
Argo-Bond	616-735	30	9	
B6	790-830	28	11	
D3	700-740	24	8	
" Sil-Fos "	625-780	45	11	Data Sheet 2131
" Silbralloy " ..	638-694	35	12	,, ,, 2132

The above table is compiled from data kindly supplied by Messrs. Johnson, Matthey & Co. Ltd. of Hatton Garden, London.

Manufacturer's Comments:
Good general purpose alloy where long plastic range and comparatively high melting point are not disadvantageous.
A eutectic-type alloy offering maximum ductility with low melting point and ability to join dissimilar metals.
An all-purpose alloy having the lowest silver content consistent with a low, short melting range and the ability to join dissimilar metals.
A quartionary alloy of general application introduced for use where a long plastic range is desirable or where the use of a high silver alloy is economically impracticable.
For use where a really long plastic range is required in an alloy of relatively low silver content possessing a reasonably low flow point.
The highest melting silver brazing alloy in the popular J.M.C. range for use where elevated temperature is met with.
Suitable for both ferrous and non-ferrous work and retained in the popular range for its intermediate melting point.
For flux-free brazing of copper or with flux on copper alloys. Unsuitable for steel or nickel alloys.
For oxy-acetylene flux-free brazing of copper at low cost. Unsuitable for steel and nickel alloys, but suitable for copper alloys with flux.

TABLE 9. BOILER EVAPORATION FIGURES

1 Imperial Gallon weighs 10 lb. and is of 277 c. in. capacity.
∴ 1 lb. water occupies 27·7 c. in.
  1 pint water occupies 34·6 c. in.

100 sq. in. (the usual unit for model boiler calculations) = $\frac{100}{144}$ sq. ft. = 0.69 sq. ft.

An evaporation of 1 c. in. per min. per 100 sq. in. of boiler heating surface will be 1·44 c. in per min. per sq. ft. = 86·5 c. in. per hour = 3·12 lb. per hour.

								c. in. per 100 sq. in. per min.
∴ An evaporation of	1 lb. per sq. ft. per hour						=	0·32
,,	,,	,,	2 lb.	,, ,, ,, ,,	,,		=	0·64
,,	,,	,,	3 lb.	,, ,, ,, ,,	,,		=	0·96
,,	,,	,,	4 lb.	,, ,, ,, ,,	,,		=	1·28
,,	,,	,,	5 lb.	,, ,, ,, ,,	,,		=	1·60
,,	,,	,,	6 lb.	,, ,, ,, ,,	,,		=	1·92
,,	,,	,,	7 lb.	,, ,, ,, ,,	,,		=	2·14
,,	,,	,,	8 lb.	,, ,, ,, ,,	,,		=	2·56
,,	,,	,,	9 lb.	,, ,, ,, ,,	,,		=	2·88
,,	,,	,,	10 lb.	,, ,, ,, ,,	,,		=	3·20
,,	,,	,,	11 lb.	,, ,, ,, ,,	,,		=	3·52
,,	,,	,,	12 lb.	,, ,, ,, ,,	,,		=	3·84
,,	,,	,,	13 lb.	,, ,, ,, ,,	,,		=	4·16
,,	,,	,,	14 lb.	,, ,, ,, ,,	,,		=	4·48
,,	,,	,,	15 lb.	,, ,, ,, ,,	,,		=	4·80
,,	,,	,,	16 lb.	,, ,, ,, ,,	,,		=	5·12
,,	,,	,,	17 lb.	,, ,, ,, ,,	,,		=	5·43
,,	,,	,,	18 lb.	,, ,, ,, ,,	,,		=	5·77
,,	,,	,,	19 lb.	,, ,, ,, ,,	,,		=	6·10
,,	,,	,,	20 lb.	,, ,, ,, ,,	,,		=	6·40